The Exchange Invest 1000

This is Copy 096.

The Inaugural List of the Most Influential People in Exchanges

and Market Structure Worldwide

By Patrick L Young

Happy Reading!

Malta 29/9/17.

The Exchange Invest 1000

The Exchange Invest 1000

The World's Most Influential People In Market Structure

Patrick L Young

DV Books

Valletta

First Published as a Limited, Numbered Edition, September 2017.

The Front Cover was designed by B.S. Traczykowska and depicts "Young's Pyramid" the way in which Patrick L Young measures the relative size of the world's markets.

To all those who have made the world's market structure.

Without you there would be a great deal less commerce

and indeed no reason for Exchange Invest to exist!

Contents

126-150

151-175

176-200

201-225

226-250

251-275

276-300

301-325

326-350

351-375

376-400

401-425

426-450

451-475

476-500

501-526

526-550

551-575

576-600

601-625

626-650

651-675

Politicians

Central Bankers

Dealmakers

Visionaries

Thinkers

Ten To Watch

Women (World)

Women USA

Women UK

Women Europe ex-UK

Women Middle East Africa & Asia

Established Entrepreneurs

StartUp Entrepreneurs

Industry Associations

Tech Gurus

FinTech

Blockchain

North America

Europe

S-E Asia

China

Subcontinental Superstars

By The Same Author

Capital Market Revolution!

The New Capital Market Revolution!

The Promiscuous Investor

Single Stock Futures A Traders Guide

The Exchange Manifesto

As Editor:

An Intangible Commodity

The Gathering Storm

Forthcoming:

Victory or Death!

About Exchange Invest

Exchange Invest is a unique daily newsletter devoted to analysing and understanding exchanges and market structure throughout the world, read by leading investors and the executives running the world's exchanges, CCPs, CSDs and related vendors et al from the very largest to the smallest.

It was founded in 2013 by Patrick L Young, a former exchange CEO and expert in the market structure field whose pioneering work in fintech dates back to a career in online WWW e-commerce starting in 1994.

You are invited to sign up for the free daily e-mail newsletter via the web site ExchangeInvest.com.

Acknowledgements

At one time or another, in bars which were once smoky and are now clear, there has been a preponderance of discussions, often at leading industry events, on just who matters in the world of exchanges.

This list is the result of several years work trying to bring together a methodology which would allow those who influence the market structure parish to be duly acknowledged.

The list itself, being the inaugural one, has stretched over more than 2 years. The calculation period for eligibility and ranking began in 2015 and ran through 2016 to late August 2017.

Countless people have assisted this process in great detail but all have been given anonymity so they cannot be held responsible for this lengthy exercise which has been initially a rather secretive process. In future years, you can expect the new Exchange Invest Most Influential Index to appear annually.

I would, however, like to particularly thank a few people including those who worked purely on production. My wife, Beata, has been a constant source of support and creative assistance. Moreover the cover by Beata Traczykowska is marvellous! Oliwia Kopinska has painstakingly tracked down all manner of data sets and processed them assiduously. Elizabeth Cortis elegantly proofread the text and has indulged my pithy whim where genuine English grammar might have been at odds with my typing.

Permit me to add that no animals were harmed in the making of this book and if it makes you feel better for your CSR principles, doubtless we recycled something and cared about the environment somewhere along the line.

Whatever the ultimate result on these pages, any errors are mine.

Correspondence will be welcome on the Index, this publication and indeed the future editions.

Please email me via Patrick@DerivativesVision.com

Finally, let me say that I thoroughly appreciate the commercial interaction of all parishioners who have sponsored Exchange Invest, bought premium subscriptions and indeed acquired copies of this book or specifically advertised within its pages. Without your support it would be a real strain to keep supporting the Exchange Invest platform.

Moreover, I must note that all EI1000 advertisements were committed "blind" as to the position of any of their staff herein.

All future commercial interactions are welcome and I look forward to receiving your subscriptions and sponsorships for Exchange Invest and encourage you to welcome me at my reasonable fees to your conferences and events to chair interviews & panels or opine on the future state of the parish, fintech, financial centres and indeed finance as a whole.

Patrick L Young

August 25th, 2017

Patrick@DerivativesVision.com

Young's Pyramid

Young's Pyramid of Exchanges
AKA A Note On The Cover
& How We Got to EI1000

When it comes to sizing exchanges, I have long deployed this simple methodology, my eponymous pyramid as shown on the front cover.

While it has been deployed at several conferences (most notably my own Young Markets where it made its first 'public' appearance), the pyramid has not been widely distributed, although I expect it will filter more into the 'mainstream!'

The Pyramid itself was first drawn up by myself as the 'for profit' and publicly listed universe expanded more than a decade back. It was a simple way to graphically represent the sheer size of exchanges and their competitors.

It therefore splits market groups into three tiers:

Tier One: the supersized leaders

Tier Two: large exchanges (a mix of public & privately held)

Tier Three: smaller markets, some new, some old... (and all the way down to the tiny platforms I first termed micro exchanges).

Thus the pyramid is a very useful and instant tool for demonstrating precisely the fact that LSE and NASDAQ are very large entities but despite a preponderance of deals, they are relative minnows by comparison to the absolute top tier players.

This segmentation has remained a valid form of demarcation with considerable movement over the years in the overall 'pecking order.'

Originally there had been around 4 major exchange groups in the top tier. This subsequently reduced to a big 3 in recent years (CME, ICE, HKEX) while DB1 gradually dropped back into the tier two peloton.

Meanwhile the second tier is a very broad affair nowadays with the largest entities such as DB1, LSE and NASDAQ dwarfing the smallest entities such as GPW (Warsaw) which hangs in on the end of this tier by dint of being still a recognisable "department store" entity with many of the same units as the larger groups, albeit at a much lower level of size.

Then we reach tier three which peaks with some fairly serious entities such as the Athens Exchange which is a great business betrayed by the national economy surrounding it and goes all the way down to tiny start up platforms which are so small as to be invisible to the naked eye for those in orbit at the top of the premier tier.

This therefore delivers a fairly simple and crisp delineation of the world of exchanges. However, that didn't answer a question which bugged me for many years: just WHO are the important people in exchanges, the influencers who can make a difference to the market across the vast cornucopia of businesses which comprise the global parish of market structure?

Alas I couldn't fit the answer into a simple diagram such as the pyramid which graces the cover of this book.

However this rather considerable volume is the first attempt to answer the question. I'll be revisiting this question with the help of my algorithms annually from now on.

Genesis Of A List

A discussion of this kind has been a recurring staple of industry conferences for years – that late evening discussion by the bar as various parties endeavour to assess who actually matters!

For over a decade, it has fascinated me to keep a rough running score of just who has significant importance in the world of market structure – or as I like to term it 'the exchange parish'. The concept was simple albeit the execution was, well, let's just call it complex!

That said, I have some 'form' in these calculations. Way back when Lehman Brothers was still solvent, I produced a list of the 500 most influential figures in the world of financial centres that was well-received at the time. Alas, the publisher of the said list didn't quite have such an enjoyable time negotiating the ensuing property collapse and banking crisis which led that list to reach a dead end along with the publication it emerged from. Nevertheless, it proved a useful learning experience, as I mastered the black art of creating such lists using feasible methodologies.

Fast forward a half decade by which time the background work on creating the Exchange Invest daily newsletter was well under way. Again, it struck me that sooner or later the time would come to create a benchmark which assessed who were the real movers and shakers shaping the future of the parish. However, it needed to be a proper, comprehensive list, not merely a cherry picker with 25, 40, 50 or 100 names – the world needed representation and that meant way over 250.

During summer 2016 I gave the project green light and a team of disparate souls began beavering away. It was a top secret affair, so much so that other staff members didn't even know about it! The EI1000 team were new to Exchange Invest, hired to deploy specific skills in the creation of a unique index which assesses the people who are most influential in the world of market structure.

At first the thesis held that a solid 500 ought to be ideal. Very swiftly it became clear that the number would have to be a round 1000 – only at that stage could the listing cover the bulk of all the world's different exchanges, markets, platforms, CSDs, CCPs, regulators and intermediaries, consultants, advisors et al. (even the media) who shape the parish on a daily basis. Even then, there are markets that have not been included. Thus, in the 2018 edition I expect to see considerable change, both in where people are ranked as well as who actually occupies the thousand slots.

If you made it into the inaugural 2017 list then rejoice and celebrate, sing the message from the rooftops at whatever height your vertigo can survive and enjoy the honour – on the obvious proviso that nothing lasts forever and this is a competitive list to gain/retain access to!

Of course, there will be some controversy over not just the ranking but also those who have been omitted. In particular, large financial centres may be surprised that they are not predominant in depth across the exchange world. However, that would be to misunderstand the core concept which is explained elsewhere in the methodology section. Moreover, many who may deem themselves to be demigods in the world of finance will be disappointed that they are barely, if at all, mentioned here. The key point to stress is the qualification that engagement with the parish of exchanges and market structure itself is what matters for this listing. Being the greatest investor on the planet won't gain you access to the EI1000 unless you can show your influence on the workings of the market structure itself.

Ultimately, somewhere in the region of 7500 people made it to stage one. A hefty bulk of names was combed through to arrive at this ultra-long list. Through a multi-stage process, eventually around 1500 names were defined as serious contenders for the list itself. Along the way, a list emerged in parallel of those who were departing the parish.

Take, for instance, Phupinder Gill. There can be no doubt that 'Gill', with his global approach to markets, had massive influence and was clearly at the 'pointy end' of the 1000 before he retired as CME CEO. However, with his current position involving attending to the delights of family old and young, he is hardly immediately influential in the exchange parish although it may be that he will return some day! At the same time, while incumbency delivers a certain amount of influence (the CEO of CME will naturally always be important in the parish!), the precise extent of their positioning is determined by the algorithm which marks everybody on influence via a depth of criteria, not merely a single position.

Naturally, defining influence is tricky and hence the algorithm behind the EI1000 is a highly complex one. Moreover, I might add, nobody except myself, Patrick L. Young, is privy to all the details of its calculation and the factors included therein.

As the 'Long List' reduced to the more workable short list of 1500, so those included in this tome broke into two separate components, as members of the EI1000 itself and as members of the 'departures' list which measures both those who have left in the past year as well as those moving on from the parish (in some cases, sadly leaving this world entirely).

As the algorithms worked away, a series of samples have been taken across time. Some have been direct, some were so subtle that only on reading this may there be a realisation amongst some industry denizens of the motive! The intention was not to act deliberately 'cloak & dagger' for the sake of pure obscurity but rather to deliver a control group. Overall, dozens of practitioners have been consulted about this list and I thank each and every one of them for their feedback; it was materially useful!

Incidentally, while some indications may have slipped into the ether, this printed format is the only way you can read the entire list in one place (or at least the only place you can read the full list legitimately, if you are reading this in a non printed digital version, it's pirate so please destroy it and buy a copy, like all market parishioners I defend my IP and appreciate your honesty).

Ultimately, there is room for debate, disagreement and in any case, the speed of movement in the parish means the list itself can only be viewed as a snapshot of the parish - in this case as it stood on 25th August 2017. Errors will be dealt with in the 2018 version while those omitted may find themselves included if they can suitably influence the algorithms in the next annual process. For, above all else, this is a living, ongoing dynamic process. The list in 2018 will likely be significantly different as news and events shape the next year. Moreover, the methodology continues to explore the most accurate measures defining influence. Some of the 1000 will inevitably not be included due to moving on, retirement or other changes. Moreover, every member runs the risk of perhaps being squeezed out of the 1000 zone by colleagues or competitors. Thus, the list will in future reflect influence during the preceding year. In the case of this inaugural list, the window of a 32 month 'introductory' period was used, which also accounts for the departure lists being somewhat longer than is anticipated in future years.

However you look at this process, it has been significantly detailed, with a lengthy period of conception and a vast amount of team effort to build this first list. We will evolve the process in future years with additional tweaks to maximise accuracy in an ever-changing world. I am, however, confident that the end result, this inaugural 2017 Exchange Invest Index of Influence, is the most comprehensive, ordered listing of the senior figures in our parish ever produced.

If you are included, please take a bow. If you aren't included and feel somewhat slighted, take a moment to consider what you might do better over the next 12 months. Moreover, there will be folks simply omitted by error. In the latter case the door is open to get in touch and stress your case - but first let's consider just how folks have already made it into the list.

What Defines Influence?

A great question. Clearly, holding a particular prestigious position delivers influence. When the head of XYZ megabourse rings, you tend to answer swiftly whereas ABC startup may struggle to attain anything like the same pickup rate.

At the same time, there is much more to being on the list than just holding a 'big' job. In the EI1000, a series of key factors have been deployed to measure overall IQ (in this case: 'Influence Quotient') of parishioners. Therefore you may add factors such as industry associations as a clear multiplier, albeit the associations themselves vary widely (measuring that criterion alone is based on a series of factors and evaluations).

Thus, high level day job incumbency is good. Membership of major bodies such as industry associations helps. Indeed, actually demonstrating an ability to influence those bodies is better still! The EI1000 makes no bones about liking thought too. Thus many of the linear processors in the parish who perhaps missed their vocation in the priesthood (by dint of being too young to inherit, insufficiently skilled for pure commerce and perhaps borderline on the military but nonetheless hold high-ish office in a bourse) may be shocked to discover their parish influence is, in real terms, low to non-existent.

Clearly execution is highly valued as well – the EI1000 is the elite of the parish and hence at the top end a really capable ability as an all-rounder trumps those who are assiduously monotasking their careers.

A curious mind is a wondrous thing in the digital age. The ability to think and the application of thought is perceived as a huge advantage in the EI1000 index. Those from outside the parish may find this unsurprising. Those entrapped by the linear, who are still grappling with the 'new-fangled' concepts of competition, demutualisation and electronic trading, will naturally be horrified (and to add insult to injury – not find themselves on the list!). A broad mind, an orientation to travel, a desire to read and above all a proven ability to debate the future of the parish or parts thereof: ALL carry extra weighting here. Being informed and reading voraciously the right subject matter helps too. I don't have to agree with you, I personally don't even have to like you, the algorithm decides... However, vision, clarity of thought and a depth of reading – all are good indicators of influence and leadership.

It has been a delight to be able to really delve into the deaths of meetings (romantically robbed of their smoke-filled history by the health and safety killjoys) and examine some of the broadly unsung heroes of the parish. There are thus a series of people who may actually be shocked, surprised or simply embarrassed to suddenly find themselves in the blinking light of transparency. In this category, you all hugely deserve your plaudits and even if your presence is as a result of a fleeting nudge in regulatory negotiations which came to my attention during computation of the index, enjoy your year in the listing. To those who managed similar inputs but remain opaque for now...apologies we missed your backroom mojo moves...we will redouble our efforts to track you for the 2018 edition!

The main subdivisions of the list can be viewed as follows (albeit there are a lot more discrete categories overall), in no particular order:

Exchange Chairmen & CEOs: Sometimes it is tricky in farther flung parts to discern just who is the more important figure in this pairing.

Bankers, Brokers & Market Makers: Probably a controversial category insofar as many who may feel their huge volumes make them very important may be excluded as a result of not being seen to influence parish affairs per se.

Regulators: A tricky category insofar as there are a great many senior regulators who appear, frankly, to be at best a touch patchy in their understanding of capital markets and exchanges at home, let alone abroad. Nevertheless, some key figures are here because of incumbency while most are present thanks to their ability to demonstrate clear thought on parish issues!

Executives: Show dynamism and industry, think a bit and engage with the parish and it becomes highly feasible to be included here even without being remotely the absolute boss of any business.

Non-Executives: Several portfolio and even single case non-execs have been included in the list. This may be partially due to their previous influence legacy as a senior manager or regulator as much as the position or company upon which board they sit. Meanwhile, some others have crept into the list partly as a result of their position but also due to their highly significant, exceptional influence outside of the parish. Equally, a great many less technical NEDs have been ignored simply because it was hard to derive their overall influence behind closed doors.

Analysts: The broadly forgotten. Two key analysts who are in essence the cheerleaders of the parish made it into the inaugural EI1000 Index – good for you! For 2018 I am considering a broader process of analyst, er, analysis which will likely result in more analysts being included.

Investors: A category which I did not engage with in the first instance for the inaugural list per se. This was in part due to the extent to which the process requires its own parametric approach, I may consider more investors for the 2018 list.

Journalists: Frankly a hard arena to really assess simply because incumbency on a few major organs can make or break many folks but the extent to which they themselves command any influence is often debatable. Rather it is often only proven when they leave said post and alas the history of the parish has been that they generally sink without trace. That said there are a few genuinely exceptional journalists in the parish, sometimes within very narrow focus areas (e.g. market data) but they deserve plaudits for being on top of their brief and having the capacity to change perceptions. Overall, the standard of domestic journalism in India puts the rest of the world to shame in the parish. Those who simply publish a lot of material reporting on markets may be upset that they have not tickled the fancy of the algorithm but actual influence is not something that executives rapidly ascribe to many journalists in the parish.

Consultants: A tricky subject as separating their DNA from an NDA leaves their actions somewhat opaque! Then again, if it has an ability to shine anywhere, Exchange Invest as a newsletter has been delving into parish opacity and spreading clarity for over four years now. To that end, on occasion, anecdotal sightings have gleaned significant amounts of data when trajectories are put together... There are a vast number of consultants out there, again those winning on the algorithm tend to be the ones focussed on thinking, let alone delivering results, as opposed to those merely building their cushy number from clustering perplexing PowerPoint slides at hapless clients.

EI1000 Index Calculation

Calculating the EI1000 Index

Without delving into the minutiae of the algorithm and its various processes, there are a series of key factors which help determine whether somebody qualifies for the EI1000 and thereafter determines their place.

The actual multiplier/factor applied to each ingredient varies in the algorithm ...and I'm keeping that proprietary IP to myself – it's written down and stored in a locked safe in a basement in a faraway place accessible only by a token on an obscure distributed ledger, seeing as you asked.

Amongst the key ingredients are the following:

Incumbency: Position – clearly the CEO of the largest exchange garners more points than the boss of a tiny one.

Industry Associations: Demonstrates parish engagement.

Thought Power: Those who can think about the parish or particular segments with clarity beyond their day-to-day business are highly valued. Reading is seen to be a boon, as is general awareness of business trends and clearly those in the parish itself both pertaining to, and beyond your own business.

Execution: To take a "Bigworld" example, if you said you were going to, say, build a wall and then didn't quite get around to it, you are liable to lose "IQ."

Thought Leadership: Articles, interviews, conference appearances where you could actually demonstrate some independence of Power-Point and show spirit and insight all help.

These are far from all the criteria but they are amongst the key factors in the algorithm itself.

The 2017 Edition

This first edition of the EI1000 Most Influential Index is a little special as it has been in calculation essentially over 32 months from mid 2015 to 2017. A number of backtests have also been run using older data to see how the results changed over time. The latter tests will not be published – only this finalised index which was settled on 25th August 2017.

The core of the algorithm and its inputs were assembled by myself, Patrick L Young during 2015 based on years of thinking around the subject (and a previous Index on the leading figures in financial centres which I compiled a decade before).

The initial long-list is the result of years of research but was specifically pushed forward during 2015/2016. Data was collated into a long list of circa 7500 names and then gradually sifted and compressed through multiple processes to arrive at a short list of 1500.

In the meantime, the short list was itself dynamic due to various parties either leaving the parish / losing Influence Points ('IP') or suddenly becoming influential through their own actions / a new position etc.

Mid-2016 I pushed the initiative to the forefront of the workflow and the work has been consistent ever since, refining and working with the list to deliver the best first edition we can feasibly manage. This involved multiple rounds of analysis and some 500 discussions with market influencers and others across the parish. Meanwhile various tweaks had to be undertaken as folk oscillated in and around the index while some left it due to resignation, retirement or being left to rest in peace. The list was fully parsed during July/August and then subject to some minor revisions due to events.

The absolutely final cutoff date for inclusion was August 25th, 2017. In fact the presses were stopped to allow for the addition of the untimely demise of former NADEX and TASE CEO Yossi Beinart who moved, alas from the "retired" list to the RIP list with a slightly longer tribute.

That said, please note several members of the list are believed to have resigned as of this final cutoff date but they have remained in the list as there has been no official announcement as to their futures.

Clearly no list can be comprehensive and doubtless readers will inform me of errors within this vast undertaking. However given the resources spent on this exercise, I believe it's a very decent first attempt. Moreover, with the revenue raised from this first edition, the intention is to invest in the second and subsequent versions.

Sundry Notes

Just before you take the plunge and begin working your way through the 1000 list itself, a few points on the list itself.

Overall, where it says "chairman" – presume chairman of the board as in the Supervisory Board sense. Folks with the title "chairman" or "president" "of the management board" have usually been described by CEO, sometimes GM or MD.

Where folk have the title MD & CEO (this is a particularly Indian titular context), I have generally abbreviated to just CEO .

Naturally, there is always an issue with the inherent quantitative easing process of titles – and indeed it's difficult to discern what in the old days were called directors whereas now at the average investment bank the best thing to say to a director level employee is usually "no milk and one sugar please". With the market structure parish, things are slightly different insofar as there are lots of ways of terming a member of a board (again supervisory / board of directors – not the management board or executive committee as it is more popularly termed in English).

To which end, you may see people termed "member of the board", "board member" or just plain old "NED" ("Non-Executive Director") all of which are intended to be broadly interchangeable. I appreciate that there are many (I have been one myself in various forms e.g. on the board of Liquidnet Europe) who are known as "INEDs" but the whole context of independence differs vastly across continents, so I have steered away from marking folk as "Independent" although many companies do delineate board members thus.

In the 1000 itself you will see I have in fact included more than 1000 names as various joint entries are given. It is sometimes tricky to split, even with the algorithm, some parties in pure influence terms, so I preferred to keep them together and thus the list ended up with slightly more than 1000 names. That said the top 100 is mathematically meticulous with precisely 100 folk therein. However, if anybody has a sound methodology for e.g. splitting the Winkelvoss twins, then it is either a work of inspired genius or involves the sort of detail I don't believe parishioners wish to read.

As that above quip intones, overall I have tried to make the text easy to follow, engaging and, where possible, fun. Most people have some form of bio data beside them. I hope for the 2018 edition to have bios of some kind beside every entrant as a new team is formed to carry the annual process of this volume forward full time. Anyway, enough of these explanations and forewords, it's time to read the 1000 itself, I wish you a pleasant journey and an interesting read.

Oh, and finally – yes, every single comment was written by "PLY" as per the daily pith in the daily Exchange Invest newsletter...

The EI1000 List 2017

1 Jeffrey Sprecher

Jeffrey Sprecher
Chairman & CEO
InterContinental Exchange

It's like this: I waded through over 7500 names. We built a lengthy process which refined in stages the long list of 1500. I wouldn't call it artificial intelligence – that's too grand – but there was a proper series of algorithms all humming away to deliver ordered results based on the mass of data we had collected. There were weeks and months painstakingly fact-checking, consulting subject experts, perusing conference presentations, industry engagements, interviews, regulatory submissions, opinion pieces and much more. However, let's make something clear – crystal clear: At no point during this entire process was the position of number one remotely open to debate. When the algorithm eventually came out with its response, the answer was, well, as unsurprising as the parish's most influential figure is deserving of the title!

Jeff Sprecher is not merely the most influential man in the world parish of exchanges, his peers also readily recognise it. A few, when discussing the concept of the E1000 paused to ponder, "So who is number one?", and when invited to think about it, they took a pause. Then, without being told the answer, they unanimously replied: "Yes, good point". A few mouthed his name theatrically just to salve their critical faculties but nobody doubted why he was number one. Primus inter pares, writ large.

There is one key reason why Jeff Sprecher is the number one most influential figure in the market structure parish and it leaves him head and shoulders above all the others in this list. It's not (just) building the Intercontinental Exchange from nothing to being the second biggest market cap of an exchange group in 20 years - and, let's face it, circa 38.3 billion dollars at the time of going to press is a serious number for any business! Nor is it the fact that only ICE manages a precise degree of execution in a way which leaves many other exchanges trailing in their wake. It isn't the deal flow either - albeit ICE is better at acquiring and integrating their purchases better than anybody else in the industry.

The answer is clearly a combination of all of the above but it distills in one single point which, in its very essence, defines influence. There is only one man in exchanges about whom a vast bulk of his peers ask, "What's Jeff doing?"*

As the InterContinental Exchange mastermind, Jeff Sprecher is at the top of his game. He has navigated his way through a host of deals with deft strategic brilliance. His considered thought is clearly visible whenever and wherever he speaks, be it in public or private.

As a side note, I must admit it was an honour to participate alongside Jeff on a panel at the Prosperity UK Brexit conference this year as he calmly but clearly explained the multiple vestiges of just why the UK needs to get its act together around Brexit.

Right now Jeff has ICE heading in an interesting direction, leading on the strategy of integrating and generating data revenue while still running a remarkably tight ship across the ICE empire. There were no major deals during the EI1000 calculation period, just a few comparatively modest acquisitions such as the fixed income index assets of BAML in June 2017, the TMX Atrium networks some weeks before and the US National Stock Exchange at the end of 2016 which provided a useful regulatory shell for future expansion. Nevertheless, the one question heard above all else in the parish which defines his influence is precisely that oft repeated "What's Jeff doing?"

**NB The answer I give to this question, by the way, is generally to the effect of, "How should I know, why don't you ask him?"*

2 Michael Spencer

Michael Spencer
CEO
NEX Group

Michael Spencer, the most successful self-made parishioner in the City of London built ICAP into a powerhouse and then extracted the digital assets in the last year to leave himself with a fascinating new vehicle: NEX Group. It's unclear quite where NEX will end up nor indeed if it will remain independent over the long term. However, whether it will serve as an acquisition vehicle or as prey for a major exchange, suddenly Michael has played himself into a fascinating role. ICAP had great potential but NEX has pure digital scale. Properly managed, NEX ought to be a remarkable engine of profit as post OTC Markets seek greater organisation and homogeneity. Moreover, as the great demon of QE finally disappears, to leave us with a new outbreak of that mysterious beast now generally only seen in economics theory textbooks: the yield curve, the possibilities are countless. NEX is a big bulbous nodule running up and down the yield curve, overseen by the man who was Conservative Party Treasurer and has a gold-plated Rolodex in Britain and across the world.

As NEX gets itself up to fighting weight, the question is clearly one of 'predator or prey' but in either case, the key defining factor for the future of NEX will be how it is masterminded by Michael Spencer. As such, his influence has reached a new peak.

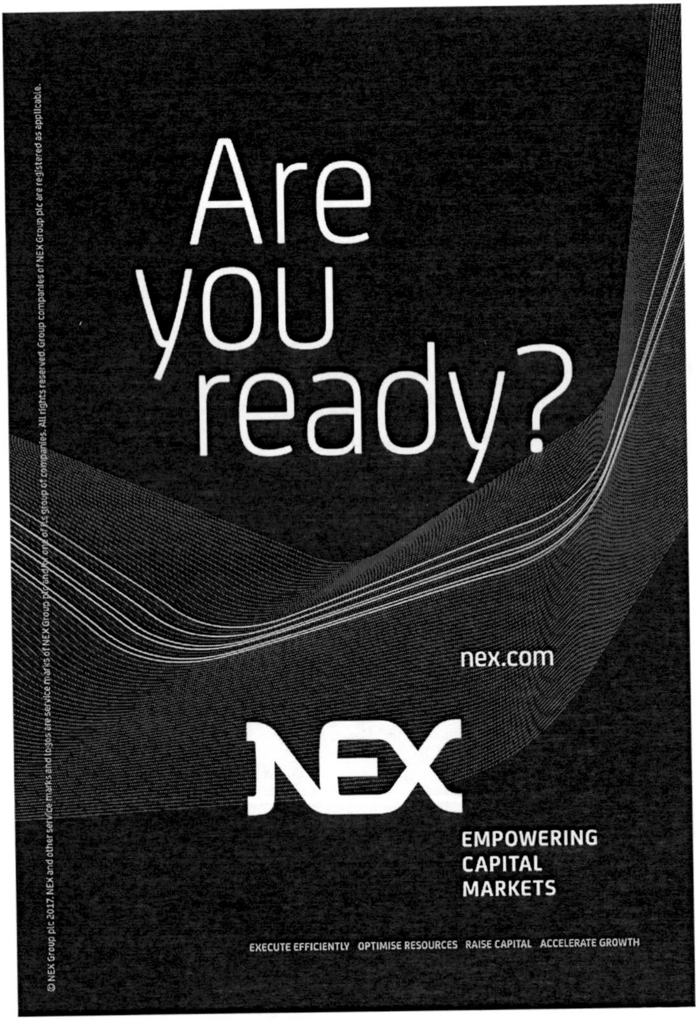
Are
you
ready?
nex.com
NEX
EMPOWERING
CAPITAL
MARKETS
EXECUTE EFFICIENTLY OPTIMISE RESOURCES RAISE CAPITAL ACCELERATE GROWTH
© NEX Group plc 2017. NEX and other service marks and logos are service marks of NEX Group plc and/or one of its group of companies. All rights reserved. Group companies of NEX Group plc are registered as applicable.

3 Charles Li Xiaojia

Charles Li Xiaojia
CEO
HKEX

Charles Li has truly ridden a rollercoaster of a career ride in recent years. Various issues made his tenure look remarkably touch and go just a few years back. However, Li has stuck to his core mission – delivering the HKEX "gateway to China" play with verve, vigour and now, a series of connections to equity and bonds on the mainland. Along the way the LME purchase may not have been a bed of roses but that exchange remains work in progress – and let's face it the real time CCP LME Clearing is a quantum leap compared to what had gone before.

Charles Li has bounced back from some relatively precarious times a few years back and has done so with a remarkable penchant for communicating including via a regular blog, his intentions to modernise the Hong Kong market and tie the city state's fortunes directly to what is a fascinating stream of linkages into the heart of the Chinese mainland.

Whereas most of the Chinese exchanges may not be noted for the colour of their leadership, Charles Li strikes a charismatic pose managing the HKEX forward as the gateway to the Chinese mainland in a trusted and historic financial centre.

4 Margrethe Vestager

Margrethe Vestager
Commissioner
DG Comp EU

Of course it is always possible DB1 will maintain their copybook of behaviour according to Einstein's definition of insanity, in which case Mrs Vestager may yet stay in this listing when the German exchange commits to another ill-fated attempt to create a monopoly. In the past year she may have rocked the world view of DB1, LSE and a great many unthinking correspondents / experts et al but it was always clear to me that she would struggle to agree to such an egregious monopoly, with or without the Brexit vote which clearly neither management team had coherently factored in.

Thus the former Danish Minister of Economic Affairs sensibly used her position as the EU's Commissioner for Competition to preclude the "Merger of Equal Desperation." Vestager may have been vilified by DB1 and LSE with rumours claiming she had at first indicated agreement with the "MOED" but her veto maintains a more sensible balance in European markets. For that benign and helpful intervention, she makes her debut in the EI1000 as the year's highest new entrant.

5 Howard W. Lutnick

Howard W. Lutnick
Chairman & CEO
BGC

One interesting thing about algorithms is that they just assess the data and don't worry about the polite niceties of life. In that sense, Howard Lutnick could be an algorithm himself. It's quite remarkable to consider this man who attracts opprobrium on something tantamount to a quantum level, has had a rather stellar few years and he shows little sign of slowing down. He sold assets to NASDAQ with aplomb and at marvellous values which have since not quite shown the promise acquirer Bob Greifeld might have hoped for. Moreover as the EI1000 Index was being completed, Howard was out of non-compete and ready to roll out his latest bond platform which he seeks to deploy to go after the likes of NEX owned EBS, Tradeweb and indeed his old eSpeed platform now under NASDAQ's suzerainty. His ability to buy GFI then strip out assets at a vast premium has only solidified his rock solid reputation as a wheeler dealer who influences the parish of market structure, even without being in a formal exchange structure.

He sold Trayport well (alas ICE have subsequently suffered under what was a rather harsh UK competition ruling, albeit par for the course with the regulator in question) and he retains Fenics lest the mood may take him to raise some cash in the near future. Life looks fascinating for Howard Lutnick - if he becomes much more successful he may even start working on a charm offensive with the many parishioners who take exception to him.

6 Adena T. Friedman

Adena T. Friedman
CEO
NASDAQ

Adena Friedman was deemed the heir apparent when she rejoined the firm in 2014 as President to oversee the technology, information, and corporate businesses that comprised over two-thirds of Nasdaq's revenues. She had served as CFO & MD of The Carlyle Group from March 2011 to June 2014, playing a significant role in taking the company public in May 2012 during what amounted to an extended sabbatical from the NASDAQ family.

La Friedman had originally joined Nasdaq in 1993 and was a key member of Nasdaq's management team for over a decade in various positions including head of corporate strategy, and CFO. She was an instrumental player in the company's acquisition strategy, overseeing the acquisitions of INET, OMX, and the Philadelphia and Boston Exchanges.

The honeymoon is ongoing. Bob has left the building entirely after a brief interregnum as Chairman and Adena has been in charge at NASDAQ since January 1. We know she practises martial arts but of the strategy moving forward and how she plans to move NASDAQ to the next level remains to be seen.

7 Donald Brydon CBE

Donald Brydon CBE
Group Chairman
LSEG

While Xavier Rolet has been almost omnipresent in the media since the 'Merger of Equal Desperation' fell apart (as Exchange Invest had confidently predicted), it's hard to really feel confident that he is truly still in power although he retains office. Equally, having burnt his bridges with so many other parish CEOs, Xavier has almost achieved the universal unpopularity of Howard Lutnick and, let's face it, Howard has been a man deemed utterly abrasive in his good moments for his entire career which has barely, if ever, involved pause for popularity.

The quiet figure at LSE HQ remains Donald Brydon who has a history of dealing succinctly from the shadows with management at other venues he has chaired (LME and the Royal Mail spring to mind immediately). Brydon also had the moral upper hand amidst what was a somewhat tawdry performance by the 'Merger of Equal Desperation' counterparties. After all, it was Donald who wrote that decent letter pondering the future of Carsten Kengeter when the insider dealing investigation emerged. Time will tell whether Brydon or Rolet will prevail but the algorithm reckons the chairman has significantly greater influence, with Xavier's currently on the wane.

8 Craig S. Donohue

Craig S. Donohue
Executive Chairman & CEO
OCC

It now seems like ancient history but let's not forget that as CME CEO from January 2004 until May 2012 Craig. Donohue led the successful completion of more than $20 billion in mergers and acquisitions, including CME's historic merger with the CBOT in 2007 and the acquisition of both NYMEX and COMEX in 2008.

Following a post CME sabbatical, Craig Donohue moved across Chicago and is now enjoying a new lease of life rejuvenating the OCC franchise at a time when there is much to play for in the development of clearing as a whole and that business in particular. The management team has been hugely reshuffled. There is an energy and sense of purpose about OCC as it deftly pushes its profile higher which had been absent for much (all?) of the entity's life to date. A new era is dawning for OCC and Craig Donohue simultaneously.

Having joined OCC in January 2014 as Executive Chairman, Craig is driven by "the goal to lead transformational change across the organization in light of OCC's designation as a Systemically Important Financial Market Utility (SIFMU) by the Financial Stability Oversight Council. His three-part strategy is focused on: 1) enhancing OCC's resiliency to systemic risk; 2) strengthening OCC's capital structure to ensure loss absorption and recovery capabilities, and; 3) reinvigorating OCC's leadership team to create a more engaged organization." After the relatively low profile of the ancient regime at OCC it is a welcome quantum leap.

9 Edward T. Tilly

Edward T. Tilly
CEO
CBOE
WFE Working Committee Chairman

Edward T. Tilly has been involved with CBOE for a lifetime. He joined the exchange as a trading floor clerk in 1987 and became a floor trader and CBOE member in 1989. He continued to trade as both a market maker and a designated primary market maker (DPM) until joining CBOE's executive management team in 2006. He was a board member from 1998-2000 and again from 2003 to 2006 while holding the highest member-elected position as CBOE's Member Vice Chairman from 2004 to 2006.

He served as CBOE's Executive Vice Chairman from 2006 to 2011 and prior to being named CEO, Tilly was CBOE President & COO from November 2011 through May 2013.

Ed surprised the parish last year with a deftly-timed, transformational takeover of BATS – a super move which gives him a shot of better technology and the chance to turbocharge many elements of the CBOE offering. This deal suggests Tilly has the sort of vision which his more linear predecessor lacked, hence he has rocketed up in influence in recent months to firmly establish himself within the top 10.

10 Lance Uggla

Lance Uggla
President
IHS Markit

The Vancouver born Lance Uggla fashioned Markit from nothing in 2003 when he spotted an opening in the CDS market which was suffering growing pains as a result of the cornucopia of messy data. As Uggla himself has noted: "Every time you have a piece of content, you can make money in different ways. And what's more important is that our customers demand this content."Thus has Markit propelled itself from a barn near St Albans ("our neighbours were sheep" one former staffer noted), to becoming a data titan in essence resolving problematic data sets where others didn't have the impetus or time to make a difference. By the time IHS and Markit merged in 2016, Markit had grown from a startup to a global public company with over 4,200 employees in 28 offices worldwide, serving over 3,000 customers.

Having engineered the IHS deal, Lance Uggla looks well placed to assume the top spot in the unified group on retirement of the CEO Jerre Stead as inferred at the time of the deal. The IHS deal gives Uggla some fascinating optionality, turning him from a potentially exposed predator into a pure play acquirer of other assets so he can spend less time looking over his shoulder.

11-15

11 Thomas Farley
President
NYSE Group

When looking at the ICE team below Jeff's office, it is fair to say that some may feel they could rank higher than Tom here but at the same time Farley is playing a great role in reminding the world that the boss of the NYSE can be telegenic, dynamic *and* charming! Influence stemming from the incumbent brand is huge here – the C-suite of NYSE has a power which is unlike that at any other exchange, barring perhaps London. ICE are proving adept owners of NYSE with Tom Farley thriving in the position. Moreover, the brand plays a huge role here – nobody, but nobody refuses a call when the NYSE president is on the other end of the line. Unless, that is, the chairman of NYSE got there first...

12 Thomas Peterffy
Chairman
Interactive Brokers LLC
NED OneChicago

Having sold off many of his original Timber Hill assets, Peterffy retains perhaps the most singularly focussed brokerage enterprise on the planet. Amongst the sell side he has no equal as either an entrepreneur or indeed in terms of being able to influence the exchange marketplace, and his voice is often heard when the industry needs a mature voice to rise above the day to day chatter.

13 Steven Maijoor
Chairman
ESMA

Steven Maijoor manages a remarkable act in the Houdini league of budgeting, even keeping ESMA going despite a parsimonious allocation of reserves and a vast workload. At the same time, he retains a sound degree of thought on the broad precepts of future regulation.

14 Jay Clayton
Chairman
SEC

His prepared opening statement, "I am 100 percent committed to rooting out any fraud and shady practices in our financial system", hardly ranks alongside the headline grabbing efforts of his Chinese counterpart Shiyu Liu but Jay Clayton has been confirmed and is in situ to shape the SEC going forward after a spell of remarkable growth in regulation itself. It is too early to tell but K-street watchers are clearly fascinated to see just how vigorous the SEC is in enforcement under the new chairman.

15 Terrence A. Duffy
Exec Chairman & President
CME Group

Some might wonder how the first joint chairman/CEO of CME has not ranked higher but then again, Terry Duffy has hardly been a highly visible presence in the parish this past year. True, he had some health issues recently but these appear, thankfully, to be resolved. At the same time, Duffy is most comfortable in Chicago and rarely seen much beyond his Midwest heartland, apart from occasional visits to Washington DC. His lack of presence in Europe or Asia saps his ability to influence, particularly as his predecessors have all had highly significant jet-setting footprints throughout the modern era of CME as a financially focussed commodity derivatives marketplace.

16-20

16 J. Christopher Giancarlo
Chairman
CFTC

Giancarlo has the industry experience to make him a potentially remarkable CFTC chairman, fuelled by what are instinctive deregulatory sentiments emanating from the White House. Few incoming CFTC Chairmen have witnessed what was tantamount to a 'rock star' welcome. Certainly, Giancarlo has a chance to reshape the industry with global repercussions...albeit he needs a few more commissioners to fill his roster first.

17 Lee Olesky
CEO
Tradeweb

Lee Olesky may not make a lot of headlines but he maintains a power of execution within Tradeweb which has propelled it to becoming a bond market powerhouse. In an era when bond platforms have been launching with alacrity, Tradeweb remains an original electronic player with the potential to maintain its foothold and add new product areas of business across the globe, including China where the firm was an early adopter of the Bond Connect system.

18 Steven Mnuchin
Treasury Secretary
US Government

Likewise on the deregulatory wave, Mnuchin has a chance to, well, I think somebody coined a phrase about making America great again at some point recently...

19 Donald Trump
President
US Government

Donald Trump, the 45th president of the United States of America may not display a lot of interest in markets but his influence stems not merely from office but his various desires to remodel the US economy, deliver tax cuts, improve infrastructure and generally deregulate. All of this is catnip to the parish if he can pull off even a fraction of this wish list.

Will he drain the swamp or will the swamp prove draining? Those are perhaps questions beyond the scope of this list. POTUS comes within the top 20 most influential in the parish as his message for financiers has been one of deregulation and that ought to serve organised markets well.

20 Shiyu Liu
Chairman
China Securities Regulatory Commission
IOSCO Member of the Board

As the South China Morning Post has noted, "When Liu Shiyu was named head of China's stock market watchdog a year ago, analysts in Beijing joked that he was taking over 'the least wanted job' in town". Certainly, Liu's approach has not been faint of heart, frequently attacking the perceived flaws of the Chinese market head on. "I was shocked by the chaos that I saw in financial markets after I came into office", is just one of his notably frank remarks. "These so-called barbarians, demons, evil creatures or financial crocodiles have taken advantage of loopholes in the system and grabbed what they want by cheating or force under the cloak of legality at the expense of small investors. We will get even with those financial crocodiles who have hurt small investors."

21-25

21 Xavier Rolet KBE
CEO
LSEG

While the PR machine has been busy championing a theme of "I'm back", in truth, Xavier Rolet's influence beyond the fawning UK Sunday papers appears on the wane. His peak was reached before the sale of Russell and the subsequent issues with the asset manager sale marked a first serious setback. The "Merger of Equal Destruction" fiasco was a shambles for LSE, losing the group valuable time and exposing what was a rather questionable series of last minute filings with the Competition authorities in Brussels. Rolet has enjoyed a spectacular career as LSE chief but the firm now needs a manager who can integrate and champion the disparate strands which have been assembled from the frenzied dealmaking which leaves LSE as a manifestly different and broader business to the entity he first became CEO of in March 2009.

22 Brad Katsuyama
Co-Founder & CEO
IEX

Brad retains influence because the "Flash Boy" aura has given him a near God-like status in the media. IEX is doing good work but the rock star reaction to his every remark remains way beyond the statistics and (impressive) growth of his IEX enterprise. Then again, if speaking truth to power makes you a star, it also delivers influence. Like IEX or loathe it, the company and its CEO have a strong ability to be heard.

23 Michael Bloomberg
CEO
Bloomberg

"Mayor Mike" may have abandoned his political ambitions but he retains considerable influence not just through his New York ties but also clearly through his influence as the head of the eponymous news and data empire which rose from nothing to challenge Reuters, giving him very significant influence across the parish.

24 Akira Kiyota
CEO
Japan Exchange Group
WFE Member of the Board

Akira Kiyota has confidently steered the unified JPX Group forward post merger. Nowadays Japan may not be seen as the vast opportunity which, say China is perceived to represent but volume remains significant and operations are efficient.

25 David Goone
Chief Strategy Officer
ICE

David Goone is the strategic brain who backs up the most strategic brain in the parish. That doesn't make him a mere backup facility, anything but; his is in the fascinating role of evaluating and also playing devil's advocate as part of the most skilled strategic management team in parish history.

26-30

26 Chris Concannon
President & COO
CBOE

The BATS boss is making an elegant transition to become COO and president of CBOE. His drive from BATS could be key to executing the strategy for the merged entity as it embraces a new realm of technology and opportunities.

27 Carsten Kengeter
CEO
DB1

In many respects, given he was still under investigation for insider dealing at the time the EI1000 went to press, it is remarkable Carsten Kengeter even makes this list at all. Whether he survives long-term as DB1 CEO remains to be seen but with the nickname "Carcrash" sticking around the parish, it is absolutely clear Kengeter's influence is not merely waning, it is almost invisible for the boss of the world's 4th largest publicly quoted exchange franchise. Perhaps like an unlucky football manager, Kengeter was just the wrong manager at the wrong time. Certainly the memos which leaked during summer 2017 from the works council suggested vast staff concern at CK1's abilities to manage DB1. In an enterprise crying out for restructuring, Kengeter's instinctive knee jerk initiative to do a deal which was simply never feasible, appears to leave him materially damaged at the time of writing.

28 John Phizackerley
CEO
TP ICAP

John Phizackerley has wasted no time aggressively pushing the TP ICAP business forward and he certainly cannot afford to rest on his laurels for even a New York minute. The initial signs have been encouraging while watching the investments of his management team in the stock is a joy to behold in a parish where too many managers just take stock grants to flip but appear unwilling to back their business acumen with their own cash.

29 Wu Qing
Chairman
Shanghai SE
WFE Member of the Board
Chairman of CEINEX

The chairman of Shanghai SE and CEINEX maintains a low profile in the West but is building a powerhouse with his exchange which also connects through Hong Kong to the world beyond China.

30 Bryan T. Durkin
CCO
CME Group
WFE Member of the Board

Many may write Bryan Durkin off as merely a great survivor of the corporate slog but his presence at CME delivers influence given that he appears to have been the man making the mileage that might be expected of the chairman/CEO. He sits on Bursa Malaysia board and was closely involved in the London CME boards until those operations were curtailed by Terry Duffy.

31-35

31 Gilson Finkelsztain
CEO
B3
WFE Member of the Board

Gilson Finkelsztain finds himself in the fascinating situation of driving forward B3, the unified Brazilian exchange enterprise which with real time clearing and CETIP being integrated is in a fascinating situation albeit mitigated by the general farrago which has been Brazilian politics. An interesting position for B3 where an outbreak of government could hugely add value to this remarkable vertical silo.

32 Chow Chung Kong
Chairman
HKEX
WFE Member of the Board

Chairman of the Hong Kong Exchange and also a member of the ExCO which is the cabinet of the island states government under its special administrative status. Make no mistake, Chow Chung Kong is absolutely at the pointy headed end of the Hong Kong A list.

33 Jos Schmitt
President & CEO
Aequitas

Jos Schmitt remains one of the leading thinkers and executors in the industry. Having sold one upstart entity to the TMX leviathan, his latest venture Aequitas is continuing to add colour to the Canadian market structure in a manner which appears to be beyond the ability of the TMX CEO to compete with. Jos thus has vast influence compared to the size of his enterprise and is currently truly the leading 'Canadian' executive in the parish.

34 Charles Vice
President & COO
ICE

Charles Vice is probably underrepresented here. If this index were a first past the post proportional vote affair, then the entire ICE management team would have occupied most every space in the 1000 up to here as Jeff Sprecher's quota was distributed. Seriously, amongst the core team members at ICE, Vice is a leading player in the world's best managed exchange enterprise.

35 Hans-Ole Jochumsen
President Global Trading & Market Services
NASDAQ

After several years in the USA, Hans-Ole Jochumsen returned to Europe at the start of 2017 having managed and learnt from his New York sojourn. An accomplished operator across the NASDAQ arena, Hans-Ole is popular and productive to deal with. His star is shining bright and his new role as top line manager, overseer and strategist in Europe places him in an ideal position to help Adena Friedman move forward with NASDAQ across the world.

36-40

36 Kelly Loeffler
SVP Corporate Communications & Marketing
ICE

Kelly Loeffler relinquished her direct IR responsibility just as we closed for press which marks a shift for ICE as she crafted the role and became the outright IR doyenne. Dynamic, driven and a confident manager, Loeffler has played a key role in the ICE story and maintains a vast portfolio with responsibility for marketing and communications.

37 Lynn Martin
President & COO
ICE Data Services

Lynn Martin combines serious execution skills with a vision to understand and appreciate as well as deliver the data strategy which is now powering much of ICE.

38 Robert Greifeld
Chairman
Virtu

With the long wave goodbye as CEO turning into one of the shortest chairmanships in living memory for any bourse, let alone NASDAQ, Bob has moved almost seamlessly to become chairman of Virtu (as we closed for press) on the completion of the deal to buy KCG.

39 David Peniket
President
ICE Futures Europe

David Peniket was Director of Finance at the International Petroleum Exchange (IPE), before its acquisition by an American entrepreneur named Jeffrey Sprecher – whatever happened to him I wonder? Prior to joining IPE in January 1999, Peniket was an accountant at KPMG.

As the boss of ICE's European operations, David maintains a relatively low profile with a high impact across the continent. He may not be voluble but his perceptions remain pinpoint accurate.

40 Andrew Bailey
CEO
Financial Conduct Authority UK
IOSCO Member of the Board

The boss of the UK regulator continues to face the usual problems of being the lead bureaucrat in a London financial centre where the Brexit vote shocked the establishment and will likely lead to significant change ahead for the FCA.

41-45

41 Joachim Faber
Chairman
DB

With German powers of incumbency as they are, Chairman Faber is probably safe in office as chairman of DB1 albeit he has had a dismal year where his influence waned considerably given his wrong-headedness on the Merger of Equal Desperation and indeed his complete inability to clearly enunciate any issues with the disgraceful situation where his CEO was investigated for insider dealing as a result of appearing to be making deals on one hand while buying DB1 stock on the other.

42 Ajay Tyagi
Chairman
SEBI

Ajay Tyagi became the 9th chairman of the Securities and Exchange Board of India early in 2017, replacing the retiring U.K. Sinha. Interestingly, Tyagi has a clear 5 year term, a luxury not afforded to many of his predecessors and while his experience in capital markets directly is limited (he is, unsurprisingly, a career civil servant), his initial steps have been encouraging in terms of trying to make Sebi more responsive and clearing up the backlog of items under consideration by the bureaucracy. Tyagi must reform but at the same time he will find it tricky to move what is essentially a reactionary socialist blob of a regulator which has an instinct towards hyperprescriptive interventionism to the point of nitpicking.

43 Alexander Afanasiev
CEO
Moscow Exchange

Alexander Afanasiev oversees one of the most competently managed echanges in the parish albeit with even more significant government issues due to the sanctions applying to Russia as a result of Crimean issues, than even his counterparts in the likes of Brazil and Greece.

44 Gerard Rameix
President
AMF
IOSCO Member of the Board

As a longstanding AMF staffer who has risen to the top, Gerard Rameix is a key player in the EU's regulatory positioning post Brexit. Term limited, he recently stepped down from the ESMA Board.

45 Ashley Ian Alder
CEO
SFC Hong Kong
IOSCO Chairman

As boss of the Hong Kong regulator, Ashley Ian Alder's position is of significance which is enhanced by his chairing of IOSCO, a regulatory body which is now truly coming of age. The challenge, of course, is dealing with the end of the regulatory cycle and finding ways to deregulate going forward which will clearly be tricky for the regulators with inherently interventionist instincts.

46-50

46 Kathleen M. Cronin
Senior MD GC
CME Group

A longstanding member of the senior CME team, Cronin has considerable influence by dint of the CME's overall size and range.

47 Scott O'Malia
CEO
ISDA

Scott O'Malia appears to have the highest profile and greatest influence amongst the industry bodies not merely by dint of his former Commissionership of CFTC (qv Walt Lukken at FIA) but as ISDA is the association of the traditional OTC side of derivatives, he has colossal influence in the parish and across banking.

48 Ryozo Himino
Vice Minister for International Affairs
FSA Japan

As a deputy minister astride the Japanese regulatory colossus, Ryozo Himino has significant clout globally.

49 Scott Hill
CFO
ICE

Scott Hill oversees the balance sheet of the ICE, pays the bills in reasonable time and above all else, ensures a steady stream of funding for all deals.

50 David Thomson
Chairman
Thomson Reuters

As chairman of Thomson Reuters, David Thomson has helped shape the new business going forward as it has almost effortlessly made a de facto HQ shift to North America while retaining its colossal roots in London.

51-60

51 Martin Scheck
CEO
ICMA

The ICMA Bond market participants have been reluctant to endorse the age of the exchange and platforms as a whole but Martin Scheck is now in a brave new world where he brings forward an efficient industry association which is finding more and more electronic platform / exchange trading across all forms of debt instruments.

52 Deirdre Somers
CEO
Irish Stock Exchange
FESE President

The happiness of Deirdre Somers' team is not in doubt given the Irish Stock Exchange's 'best employer' awards this past year. Moreover, as chairman of FESE she has been hugely influential and, given her original push for SME funding, she is the right chairman at the right time of that organisation in an era when the EU needs to get a broad Capital Markets Union running asap if the EU is to be given a sporting chance of survival.

53 Kimberly S. Taylor
President
Global Operations Technology & Risk
CME Group

Kim Taylor, like so many CME managers, benefits in this index from her length of tenure.

54 Trevor Spanner
Group CIO
HKEX

Trevor Spanner has had a good year, pushing LME projects ahead and more recently being promoted in Hong Kong to group CIO as the HKEX group reaches an exciting point in the genesis of its next generation IT solutions.

55 Adrian Farnham
CEO
LME Clear

Adrian Farnham runs LME's state of the art real-time CCP from London, a project which injects confidence into the metals markets' various regional players across the world's time zones.

56 Matt Chamberlain
CEO
LME

Matt Chamberlain has already acquitted himself well at his first London IDX albeit the panel was skewed against him insofar as content ranged around that nearly extinct beast – the mega merger – as well as the clearing of Euro denominated financial instruments. Matt is in an interesting position as the new CEO of LME, replacing Garry Jones. His brainpower is not in doubt and he has the capacity to think strategically. It will be interesting to watch his performance in the coming year.

57 Paul P. Andrews
Secretary General
IOSCO

The veteran FINRA boss Paul Andrews 'retired' from FINRA to join IOSCO just as that entity is blossoming in significance.

58 Pierre Moscovici
Commissioner Economic & Financial Affairs
EC

With a broad commission portfolio, Moscovici is influential in one of the EU's key areas of suicide note generation, the Financial Transaction Tax.

59 Brad Peterson
CIO
NASDAQ

Given the complexity of NASDAQ's multiple systems, Brad Peterson oversees a complex technology stack.

60 Greg Medcraft
Chairman
ASIC
IOSCO Member of the Board

Sydney newspapers have been suggesting that for a while Greg Medcraft has been looking to live in Paris in the near future when he steps down from ASIC where he has long been the lead figure.

61-70

61 Li Zhengqiang
Chairman
Dalian Commodity Exchange

Li Zhengqiang runs one of the biggest commodity derivatives markets in the world which most every western trader currently never even thinks of every day.

62 Walter Lukken
President & CEO
FIA

Walt Lukken remains an amiable and popular figure in the industry association nexus. He has generally integrated the new global FIA entity while maintaining a lot of the core futures industry constituency and endeavouring to reach out to the broader world of derivatives in a CCP centric, post OTC world.

63 Ashishkumar Chauhan
CEO
BSE India
Chairman of SAFE

Ashishkumar Chauhan finds himself CEO of Bombay SE at a fascinating moment – for the first time since its foundation, the NSE is suffering setbacks. That deals a huge opportunity for BSE to succeed and indeed at any other time in the past 20 years, the most important Indian executive in the parish would clearly have been from NSE.

64 Vikram Limaye
CEO
NSE India

After the remarkable exit of Chitra Ramkrishna and the subsequent HFT investigation which claimed the vice chairman and former CEO Ravi Narain, Vikram Limaye endured what seemed like an interminable delay in being confirmed by Sebi as suitable for the post...just before the EI1000 closed for press. Limaye has a stunning pedigree as a banker prior to joining NSE as the first outsider to run the business. With an IPO looming, first he has to re-establish confidence in NSE which has endured a tough year.

65 Rick Holliday-Smith
Chairman
ASX

As the power at ASX, Rick Holliday-Smith has a unique ability for maintaining his monopoly Australian entity.

66 Thomas Hammond
President
ICE Clear US

Tom Hammond oversees the US clearing business of ICE while thinking about the future of clearing – which is far from the workaday average of many CCP bosses.

67 Joe Ratterman
Member of the Board
CBOE & Axoni

Now a board member of CBOE but never to be forgotten as one of the team founders which powered BATS from just another ECN to being a veritable execution phenomenon in markets either side of the Atlantic.

Joe became the sole independent NED, at Axoni, a distributed ledger technology company just as the EI1000 went to press.

68 Verena Ross
Executive Director
ESMA

Verena got to ESMA on the back of her UK experience but now is presumably pivoting to represent her German nationality given the impending Brexit which will see the UK regulator likely lose direct access to ESMA positions.

69 Janet Yellen
Chairman
US Federal Reserve Board

Janet Yellen says there is not likely to be a repeat of a major financial crisis in the near future – let's hope that that is one thing the Central banker can get right...as otherwise the nature of a major crash may prove challenging to the very future of central banking itself.

70 Nils-Robert Persson
Chairman
Cinnober

The intellectual driving force behind Cinnober, Nils-Robert Persson has overseen the creation of the world's largest independent exchange software vendor. With a clear lead in much of the real time clearing stack, Cinnober is seeking to take advantage beyond the parish as well as within, spinning off a new enterprise to look at clearing tech for clients.

71-80

71 Ronan Ryan
President & Co-Founder
IEX

The NY domiciled Irishman is a leading figure in the Flash Boys narrative which has built elegantly to a 2% presence in the US stock market with the lure of a listing franchise coming soon.

72 Nicky Newton-King
CEO
JSE
Member of the Board WFE

Nicky Newton-King has found herself under pressure from competition as upstarts seek to attack the JSE's monopoly. Criticism of the JSE's rather high-handed initial approach in seeking to preclude the new platforms ought to be balanced against a need for a more even-handed approach to who shoulders the regulatory burdens where the JSE has a rather significant amount of the burden. Nicki is stewarding the JSE ship remarkably well given the abject incoherence of much of the government in the Republic of South Africa.

73 Liu Nengyuan
President & CEO
Shanghai Futures Exchange (SHFE)

"Daily liquidity on SHFE is surpassing that of the LME and Comex put together. The highest monthly trading volumes for copper and zinc last year were on the SHFE, according to Macquarie", Henry Sanderson noted in the FT in April 2015. Since then it has grown. Do we need to know more about the CEO and president of the Shanghai Futures Exchange to discern his influence? I think not...even if it may be a local volume power, his position at SHFE delivers him significant influence.

74 Finbarr Hutcheson
President
ICE Benchmark Administration

With his accession to a leading role in clearing within ICE (in Europe) Finbarr has a broad industry experience from his LIFFE times through the ICE benchmark business to now overseeing a greater clearing remit.

75 Andreas Preuss
Deputy CEO
DB
Member of the Board WFE

Veteran British Parliamentarian Enoch Powell noted how "all political careers end in failure" and in a somewhat velvet-lined fashion, that is now the outlook for Andreas Preuss. It remains to be seen whether his contract is given any renewal against a background where DB1 has significant numbers of management in danger with Jeff Tessler already signalling his departure. In the end, Andreas appears to have retained a stubborn fixation for acquiring the London Stock Exchange yet the Merger of Equal Desperation was never credible, no matter how much the DB1-LSE agitprop machine sought to marginalise those who were capable of individual thought. In many respects, Andreas' status in the industry probably gives him a higher rating this year than he deserves as it looks fair to suggest his time in the parish will end soon. Then again he might turn out to be the stop gap CEO of DB1 in a post Kengeter interregnum if CK1 falls on his sword in the event of charges...

76= Roger Lee
Joint COO
HKEX

76= Calvin Tai Chi Kin
Joint COO
HKEX

The joint COO's of HKEx have firmed their grip on executive responsibility this past 12 months and are responsible for the execution of what is an aggressive strategy across the bourse group which continues to extend its ties to China through various initiatives.

78 Alexey Kudrin
Chairman
Moscow Exchange

MOEX remains one of the best run operations in the exchange world under the suzerainty of Chairman Kudrin. Sanctions and a general anti-Russian sentiment continue to weigh on the marketplace but Kudrin's influence remains strong following his lengthy stint as Russian Finance Minister a decade ago.

79 Pier Carlo Padoan
Minister of Finance
Government of Italy

The man whose act actually killed the Merger of Equal Desperation by placing a question mark over a deal which involved the MTS bond platform. Ultimately it was Margrethe Vestager who wielded the knife but Pier Carol Padoan was a touch akin to Banquo's ghost at the press conference where the EU Commissioner lashed some of the remarkable antics by the parties to the Merger of Equal Desperation.

80 Paul Atkins
CEO
Patomak

As an architect of the Trump financial team in the transition, former Commissioner Paul Atkins has remarkable influence over US policy and, given that he is a supporter of free markets, he is a welcome pro market influencer in Washington.

81-90

81 Michael Piwowar
Commissioner
SEC

Piwowar performed strongly as acting chairman awaiting the confirmation of Jay Clayton and has laid down many sensible vestiges of the precepts for a successful deregulatory wave under the Trump Presidency.

82 Sharon Y. Bowen
Commissioner
CFTC

In many respects the most welcome surprise of the CFTC Commissioners in recent years, Bowen is pragmatic, holds sensible anti-protectionist views on Euro clearing and has been active in trying to rein in the egregious fiasco which is forex dealing, particularly in the retail domain. Sadly standing down in the near future.

83 Richard Sandor
Chairman & CEO
American Financial Exchange

The man who created modern financial futures, environmental futures and did more to revolutionise the parish than anybody in this list, the Doc is busy running American Financial Exchange which is a brilliant market for the real economy and the small to mid-size banking market across the USA.

84 Kara M. Stein
Commissioner
SEC

As an advocate for a more digital SEC, Stein may be able to forge a progressive consensus for a better market structure albeit the ghastly festering legacy of the Reg NMS mess will take a long time to resolve.

85 Hu Zheng
CEO
China Financial Futures Exchange
CEINEX Board Member

Hu Zheng sits on the Supervisory board of DB1 jv CEINEX as well as being CEO of CFFEX. Has a wealth of experience in Chinese exchanges in multiple products based in Shanghai.

86 Wang Jianjun
President & CEO
Shenzhen Stock Exchange

After seven years with the CSRC, Wang Jianjun joined Shenzhen Stock Exchange as the new CEO replacing Song Liping who was the first female head of the Shenzhen Exchange and spent eight years in office building SZSE to the world's 8th largest stock market by market capitalisation.

87 Zhang Shenfeng
Chairman
China Financial Futures Exchange
CEINEX Supervisory Board

Zhang Shenfeng is chairman of CFFEX and sits on the supervisory board of CEINEX, the DB1 jv.

88 Huang Hongyuan
President
Shanghai Stock Exchange
CEINEX Supervisory Board

Huang Hongyuan became president of Shanghai Stock Exchange (SSE) after a wealth of experience in banking and the CSRC, joining Shanghai SE as EVP in 2011 and being elevated to president in 2012. He is a member of the board of CEINEX.

89 Wu Lijun
Chairman
Shenzhen Stock Exchange

When Chen Dongzheng retired in 2014, Wu Lijun replaced him as chairman of the Shenzhen Stock Exchange. Previously Wu Lijun had served as assistant to the then CSRC boss Xiao Gang and as a member of the CSRC Communist Party committee.

90 Mrugank M. Paranjape
CEO
MCX India

Under Mrugank Paranjape MCX looks to be regaining its swagger after the vast problems left behind by the impact of the NSEL saga which forced the exit of FTIL from the management and shareholder roster.

91-100

91 John McPartland
Senior Policy Advisor
Financial Markets
Federal Reserve Bank of Chicago

A low profile does not have to infer 'low influence'. That said, the generally reticent John McPartland will probably be aggrieved to see any transparent light being shone on his position. However, in the USA he is Mr CCP and his expertise shapes thinking throughout the world.

92 Orrin Hatch
Chairman
Senate Finance Committee

Orrin Hatch is the most senior Republican Senator having represented Utah since 1977. As Finance Committee Chairman he has a key role to play in what may emerge from the Trump deregulation agenda.

93 Michael Dawley
MD
Goldman Sachs
FIA Chairman

Perhaps slightly lower than may be anticipated but clearly fully deserving of being in the elite top 100 tier of parishioners. Dawley runs a GS derivatives business alongside his active chairmanship of FIA.

94 Stephane Boujnah
CEO
Euronext

Influential as the boss of a large multinational in the second tier, albeit sometimes struggling to keep his French 'stakeholder' happy with their machinations, Stéphane Boujnah has an interesting approach to Euronext and is pushing the business ahead, emphasising it can survive independently.

95 Shozo Ohta
President & CEO
Tokyo Financial Exchange

At the helm of the exchange which trades Japanese short term interest rates, clearly an outbreak of a yield curve would be a sensational growth spur for the TFE which manages STIR derivatives in the world's third largest free trading currency.

96 Michael Ptasznik
EVP
CFO NASDAQ

Ptasznik sits on top of the finances of a complex series of subsidiaries within NASDAQ, none of whom seem to be very prompt to pay their bills.

97 Cicero Augusto Vieira Neto
COO
B3

Cicero Augusto Vieira Neto has been COO since 2008 at what is now B3.

98 Bill Huizenga
Chairman
House subcommittee on capital markets securities & investments

Bill Huizenga is in the forefront of the battle against Dodd Frank.

99 Lee Hodgkinson
Head of Markets & Global Sales, CEO Euronext London
Euronext
FESE Vice-President

The key free marketeer in the Euronext organisation. Runs London and maintains a high profile across cash and derivatives markets. Unlucky to miss out on the top job at Euronext but a high profile and likeable figure who is doing an excellent job as vice president of FESE on top of his multifaceted Euronext roles which has included building out the deals in the likes of EuroCCP, Algomi and FastMatch.

100 Wen-Chang "Peter" Chiu
CEO
Taiwan Futures Exchange Corporation

Joined TAIFEX as a director in 2001, becoming CEO in 2013 of the Taiwan Futures Exchange.

101-125

101 Mitch McConnell
House Majority Leader & Member of the Senate Agricultural Committee

As House Majority leader, Mitch McConnell is rarely out of the headlines while his position as an Agriculture committee member makes him important to the parish.

102 Michel Barnier
Chief Brexit Negotiator
EC

The making of Barnier will be how pragmatic he can be in dealing with the Brexit talks in order to avoid mutually assured destruction. Has a Gallic flair for wanting to control markets but appears to be more level headed than many of the Euro diehards. It will be interesting to see how well he can steer both the negotiations as well as how well he can deal with the often erratic EU institutions of President Juncker and the EuroParl.

103 Elisabeth Roegele
Executive Director Securities Supervision
BaFin
ESMA Supervisory Board; IOSCO Member of the Board

BAFIN bigwig on ESMA and IOSCO boards who once worked at the Baden-Wuerttemberg exchange (part of Boerse Stuttgart).

104 Mario Draghi
President
ECB

"Super Mario" still looks a touch tarnished having failed to secure Euro resolution but he is at least keeping things hanging together in the tricky world of the flawed single currency. Has influence in Brexit and again needs to show he will be able to deploy his Europhilia to persuade the ultras that they are only going to damage the EU as much as the UK in a dogmatic protectionist approach to Brexit.

105 Vinnie Viola
Chairman Emeritus
Virtu

Vinnie Viola is in a form of limbo at the time of writing. The KCG deal completed as the EI1000 went to press which has left Vinnie Viola on the board of Virtu . He retains the title Chairman Emeritus with Bob Greifeld having taken on the Chairman's office. Earlier in 2017 Viola opted out of taking up the position as Secretary of State for the Army in the Trump administration. Given his position in the creation of Virtu and his previous NYMEX experience et al, Viola is in an influential position across the parish.

106 Jeb Hensarling
Chairman
House Financial Services Committee

A Texan chairing the House Financial Services Committee, he is close to the banking industry and broadly opposes banking regulation.

107 Giuseppe Vegas
Chairman
CONSOB
ESMA & IOSCO Member of the Board

Top Italian regulator who is on both the board of IOSCO and ESMA (replacing France's Gerard Rameix at the end of his term in July 2017).

108 Chan Woo Jeong
Chairman & CEO
KRX
Member of the Board WFE

The CEO of Korea Exchange (KRX) is also on the board of the WFE but his position became precarious recently with a likely end point looming just as we closed for press. Given some close ties to former President Park Geun-Hye, Mr Jeong tendered his resignation as the political climate remains febrile amid all manner of accusations of corruption, none of which had been levelled at the KRX boss but which resulted in a jail sentence for the head of Samsung the day after Mr Jeong tendered his resignation. In office since October 2016, he was due to remain in post to the end of September 2019.

A resignation letter sent to employees demonstrated a degree of class which has perhaps been absent in some other parish C-suites during recent years. Mr Jeong noted: "A new administration has started and I have decided to leave the KRX in the belief that we should not put new wine into an old bottle."

"Given the KRX chief post is responsible for running Korea's capital market, I will continue my job until my successor takes office."

109 Michael McClain
MD & GM Equity Clearing
DTCC

Michael McClain joined DTCC in April 2017 from OCC, where he was COO and part of the office of the Executive Chairman (Craig Donohue).

110 Patrick Combes
Chairman & CEO
Tradition

A money-broking veteran who controlled Viel and then acquired Tradition. Seeking to maintain it in the digital age as the leading IDB based on the continent of Europe.

111 K Michael Conaway
Chairman
House Agricultural Committee

The 7 term Texas Congressman chairs the House Agricultural Committee.

112 Pat Roberts
Chairman
Senate Agricultural Committee

The first man in history to chair both the House and subsequently the Senate Agricultural Committee, the Kansas Senator noted at the Fed's 2017 Ag Symposium in June: "The agriculture sector needs a government that helps maintain the competitiveness of the commodities that are grown by seeking out new and emerging markets; a federal partner that helps improve efficiencies by rolling back costly regulations; and one that helps agricultural, rural, and farm and ranch businesses plan for long-term growth by providing a permanent tax code, as well as providing producers with the tools needed to manage market uncertainties."

113 Jens Weidmann
President
Bundesbank
Chairman of BIS

Jens Weidmann chairs the Bundesbank and the BIS. Fairly quiet in recent public utterances although thought to have been very sceptical about the ECB's "whatever it takes" policy.

114 Datuk Seri Tajuddin Bin Atan
CEO
Bursa Malaysia

CEO of Bursa Malaysia since 2011. Datuk Seri Tajuddin Bin Atan is a director of all the subsidiary companies within Bursa Malaysia Group including chairman of Bursa Malaysia Derivatives and its subsidiary as well as chairman of the Exchange Committee of Labuan International Financial Exchange

115 Michael C. Bodson
President & CEO
DTCC

Michael C. Bodson is president and CEO of DTCC plus DTCC's principal operating subsidiaries, DTC, FICC and NSCC as well as being a member of DTCC's Board of Directors. Previously COO, Bodson originally joined DTCC in 2007 as Executive MD for Business Management and Strategy. Prior to this, he held a number of senior management positions with Morgan Stanley over a 20-year period.

116 Essa Abdulfattah Kazim
Governor
DIFC
Chairman DFM & Bourse Dubai NED NASDAQ

Essa Abdulfattah Kazim is a pivotal figure in Dubai, as chairman of DFM as well as governor of the DIFC and overseas holding a position on the main NASDAQ Board.

117 J. Ravichandran
Group President
NSE India

It may be that this is as influential as it gets for J. Ravichandran but he found himself unexpectedly holding the fort at NSE when Chitra

Ramkrishna abruptly resigned as he was made interim CEO, a position which was extended when incoming CEO Vikram Limaye found his regulatory acceptance delayed because - only in India - Sebi regulators were uncomfortable about Limaye's influential role in cricket.

118 Aime Ruiz Sacristan
Chairman
BMV

Aime Ruiz Sacristán caused near chaos this year when as chairman of Mexico's exchange, he presided over the listing of IEnova stock whose DG is his identical twin brother, Carlos. Fortunately, they tend to wear different coloured ties when together in public to help addled journalists and others struggling to tell the energy company boss from the bourse chairman.

119 Ashok Chawla
Chairman
NSE India

Former Competition Commission of India Chairman, Ashok Chawla has had a veritable baptism of fire since joining NSE as chairman in early 2016, for a three year term replacing SB Mathur. The CEO has resigned, the HFT investigation is still not resolved as we head to press with the EI1000 and the Deputy Chairman and former CEO Ravi Narain has resigned as well as the IPO being (understandably) delayed. Chairman Chawla appears to be keeping things turning along and he weathered the delay in confirming incoming CEO Vikram Limaye to boot while making loud proclamations that the long awaited NSE IPO will still take place. Certainly his next year may not be as action packed as the last one but it will not be dull either...

120 Olivier Guersent
DG Financial Stability Financial Services & CMU
EC

Having held the position of deputy director-general since July 2014,

Olivier Guersent was appointed to the role of Director-General for Financial Stability, Financial Services and Capital Markets Union with the EC in September 2015.

121 Benoit Cœure
Member of the Executive Board
ECB

A vocal advocate of some slightly contorted Euro protectionist approaches, particularly to derivatives clearing.

122 David Warren
CFO
LSEG

The former NASDAQ CFO appears more comfortable at LSEG but then again the venerable London bourse may soon be headed for considerable management shake-up when the lessons of the failed Merger of Equal Desperation are finally taken into account.

123 John Berrigan
DDG Financial Stability Financial Services & CMU
EU

CMU seems to be slowing its momentum, largely due to the Anglo Saxon pro-market ethos of UK membership evaporating, leaving the major nations as a fuzzy protectionist blob but Berrigan has a good standing in Brussels and holds responsibilities for key parish areas in financial stability and CMU.

124 Harris Brumfield
Chairman
Trading Technologies

As the majority owner and chairman of TT, Harris has patently made a few foes over the years and partly on account of that as well as his software's reach across markets, he has significant influence.

125 Robert Druskin
Chairman
DTCC

Robert Druskin served as Executive Chairman from April 2011 to December 31, 2015 and was previously interim CEO and Chairman of e*Trade, having earlier worked for Citigroup for over 15 years.

126-150

126 David Casterton
Vice Chairman
TP ICAP

Over at TP ICAP, David "Clumpy" Casterton has become vice chairman with immediate effect as this list was closing for press and is the most senior former ICAP figure in the management, a welcome and deserving position which will see David work to support the regional and global product and function heads within TP ICAP and continue to sit on the group's Global Executive Committee (GEC) while relinquishing his role as CEO of Global Broking for ICAP

127 Neal Brady
CEO
Eris Futures

Perhaps the clearest thinker amongst the many SEF bosses, Neal Brady has that visionary quality which has helped make Eris, the only independent platform to yet show any significant breakthrough...and in the case of Eris it has been a highly significant breakthrough, thanks to good execution allied to an intelligently thought through product.

128 Caroline Silver
MD
Moelis

In many ways the doyenne of bankers in the parish. No big deals in the past year but always on the speed dial of most every major parish exec.

129 Chi-hsien Lee
President
Taiwan Stock Exchange

Former TPEx chairman Chi-Hsien Lee became president of the Taiwan SE in 2016 as part of a management restructuring.

130 Martin Egan
Global co-head of primary and credit markets
BNP Paribas
Chairman ICMA

Clearly, as chairman of ICMA, Martin Egan has significant influence over the bond market structure.

131 Peter Hiom
Deputy CEO
ASX

Permanently overlooked for the CEO position of ASX, the question is: Will Peter seek to continue with ASX or might he consider retirement? He has done very well out of ASX, having previously worked for LIFFE in London.

132 Valdis Dombrovskis
VP & Commissioner for Financial Stability Financial Services & CMU EC

Overseeing many aspects of the financial services portfolio in Brussels including Euro clearing makes Dombrovskis a key player in the parish even though he rarely showed any interest in capital markets as PM of Latvia before his EU elevation.

133 Yves Mersch
Member of the Executive Board
ECB

Luxembourg lawyer Yves Mersch was educated at the Sorbonne and has held a multiplicity of mostly financially related regulatory posts before becoming a member of the Executive Board, European Central Bank in December 2012.

134 Chris Isaacson
EVP Global CIO
CBOE

Chris Isaacson is in many ways the most important man in the transition of CBOE as he continues to run BATS technology, only now it also powers much of the CBOE offering.

135 Lieve Mostrey
CEO
Euroclear

As CEO of perhaps the most exciting takeover target in the parish, Mostrey has a fascinating role albeit overseeing a fairly sclerotic management structure where she is primus inter pares of the multiple tiers of Belgians permanently processing but perhaps not so fixated with the future as a non bank utility outright for profit entity might be...

136 Len-Yu Liu
Chairman
Taiwan Futures Exchange Corporation

Len-Yu Liu is chairman of Taiwan Futures Exchange Corporation. They "only" managed their second best year in history last year but at 242 million contracts it is tough to ignore their influence with products to licence and the power to licence others' markets for the local marketplace.

137 Robert W. Cook
President & CEO
FINRA

A former SEC Director of the Division of Trading and Markets, Cook joined as FINRA CEO from Cleary law firm Gottlieb Steen & Hamilton LLP.

138 Jun-Ji Shih
Chairman
Taiwan Stock Exchange

Chairman Jun-Ji Shih joined Taiwan Stock Exchange in 2016 after serving in several regulatory roles including a stint as the commissioner of the Fair Trade Commission, chairman of the Financial Supervisory Commission, and minister without Portfolio of the Executive Yuan.

139 Rainer Riess
DG
FESE
NED Moscow Exchange

Rainer maintains his position as FESE Director General and also holds a seat on the board of MOEX. He has proven a popular and highly capable DG of FESE, learning the ropes around Brussels having been well schooled in the parish during his long tenure with DB1.

140 Anna Kuznetsova
MD Securities Market
Moscow Exchange

Listings can be hard to find in Russia but where there's a will there's a way. Kuznetsova oversees the Russian cash market which has many fascinating names amongst its content but still lacks the maturity of a more established market.

141 Romeo Lacher
Chairman
SIX

Romeo Lacher appears to have wasted no time in his initial six months as chairman. The CEO is stepping down and there appears to be a vigorous movement for change in Zurich's bourse and market data behemoth.

142 Christoph Boschan
CEO
CEESEG

Handed the chance to run the ailing Austrian bourse, Christoph is giving his best shot at re-establishing the business with Petr Koblic and Ludwig Nießen playing key roles.

143 Sabine Lautenschläger
Member of the Executive Board
ECB

A former Buba VP, Lautenschläger has been a permanent opponent of the OMT policy of the ECB.

144 Chen Huaping
Chairman
Zhengzhou Commodity Exchange

Chen Huaping is chairman of Zhengzhou Commodity Exchange.

145 Jose Oriol Bosch Par
CEO
BMV

José Oriol Bosch Par has been CEO of the Mexican Stock Exchange BMV since January 1st, 2015. He has experience in the financial and banking sector and held executive positions in Mexico.

146 Petr Koblic
CFO
CEESEG
FESE Member of the Board

Lively, entertaining and never short of a reasoned opinion, Petr Koblic has done an excellent job stabilising the Prague Stock Exchange (he remains CEO as well as sitting on the parent CEESEG board as CFO) and helping it grow, alongside (or perhaps at times, in spite of) its Austrian parent. Now a key member of the management team of the CEESEG, Koblic can do great things alongside CEO Christoph Boschan.

147 Dominic Stevens
CEO
ASX

The 'new' CEO of ASX has so far not been as voluble as his passive aggressive predecessor Elmer Funke-Kupper but the real power at ASX is still deemed to be behind the executive offices with Chairman Rick Holliday-Smith. ASX needs reform but the ethos appears to be a desperate attempt to cling to the status quo.

148 Loh Boon Chye
CEO
SGX

IPOs are on the up in Singapore and the exchange looks a bit more chipper as it integrated the Baltic Exchange purchase etc. However, Loh Boon Chye remains a remarkably low profile figure. He is CEO of a major publicly listed company but it is tough to really say whether he has influence or not until more evidence is available that he is not merely a part passenger on the deck.

149 Jiao Jinpu
Chairman
Shanghai Gold Exchange

A former central banker running an influential and ambitious exchange in gold.

150 Tim Mahoney
CEO
BIDS Trading

BIDS CEO Tim Mahoney has had a great year. His US franchise continues to maintain a decent and profitable market share while his deal with BATS Europe to create the LiS (Large In Scale) platform has been simply stunning even after just a few months in operation.

151-175

151 Hironaga Miyama
Chairman & CEO
Japan Securities Clearing Corporation

Hironaga Miyama is a former MD at the Tokyo SE who became the head of the JSCC in June 2013.

152 Muthukrishnan Ramaswami
President
SGX

Seen by some as the ultimate survivor in the SGX empire. Not quite attaining the mythical status of the ravens of whom it is said when they leave the Tower of London will collapse, but you get the gist.

153 James C Smith
CEO
Thomson Reuters

A relatively low profile CEO of the world's most notable independent data vendor, James C Smith was promoted to the office in January 2012

Jim began his career as a journalist and rose through the ranks at Thomson Newspapers to become responsible for operations in North America. He then led a number of professional publishing businesses serving the legal, regulatory and academic markets. He served as global head of Human Resources before becoming COO of The Thomson Corporation. Following the acquisition of Reuters in 2008, Jim ran the Professional division of the combined company.

154 Wang Fenghai
CEO
Dalian Commodity Exchange

Wang Fenghai was elevated from deputy GM to become CEO of the Dalian Commodity Exchange in June 2016 replacing Feng Bo.

155 Mark Hemsley
EVP & President Europe
CBOE

As European head of BATS, Mark Hemsley has built the business out further while now being in a key position to help CBOE expand in Europe. He has considerable derivatives experience from his time with LIFFE making him a valuable regional boss for CBOE as a group.

156 Kwa Chong Seng
Chairman
SGX

Former ExxonMobil Asia Pacific chairman and managing director Kwa Chong Seng became chairman of SGX in September 2016 replacing former Singapore Airlines CEO Chew Choon Seng.

157 Luc Bertrand
Vice Chairman
National Bank Financial Group

The key thinker in the TMX organisation (albeit from a non-executive standpoint nowadays). The moment Luc was not delivered the CEO position he deserved, was the moment they began the process of losing the plot. Interesting to see Luc buying stock earlier this year – he holds sway across both Montreal and Toronto as well as across the parish world.

158 Anneli Tuominen
DG FIN_FSA
Vice-Chairman ESMA

Finnish Regulator Anneli Tuominen became vice chairman of ESMA in January 2016 replacing Portugal's Carlos Tavares.

159 Ahmed Bin Sulayem
Chairman
DGCX

Ahmed Bin Sulayem is executive chairman of the DMCC Free Zone and Chairs DGCX as it is part of the DMCC portfolio he has played a pivotal role in developing.

160 Rashid bin Ali Al-Mansoori
CEO
Qatar Stock Exchange
WFE Member of the Board

Rashid bin Ali Al-Mansoori is perhaps best known in the parish for hosting a rather lavish WFE AGM – albeit that merits little influence in the overall world of exchanges per se. It will be interesting to see what the longer term ramifications of the Qatari diplomatic standoff with its neighbours will be for the relatively fledgling capital market structure.

161 Suneel Bakhshi
CEO
LCH Group

CEO of LCH Clearnet which remains perhaps the parish entity most desperately in need of a technology upgrade. Then again is it in the hands of Xavier or Suneel to order the upgrade? Some say only the punchcards can tell.

162 Antonio J. Zoido Martinez
Chairman & CEO
BME

A great survivor, it remains unclear when the Zoido age might end or indeed who his successor will be.

163 Gaurang Desai
CEO
DGCX

Gaurang has steered the DGCX organisation with gusto, making it a highly credible entity in the Gulf States despite it being one of very few exchanges not expressly backed by the local government. The granting of ESMA CCP approval was one excellent piece of news in 2017 followed by the summertime announcement of an MOU with ADX to create a CCP.

164 Robert Scharfe
CEO
Luxembourg Stock Exchange
FESE Member of the Board

Robert Scharfe oversees Luxembourg's thriving mix of listings which makes it amongst Europe's leading primary markets.

165 Samir Shah
CEO
NCDEX

NCDEX was losing ground to FTIL until the quite remarkable implosion of the Jignesh Shah empire but Samir Shah appears to be stabilising the situation while India awaits a more stable and pragmatic SEBI approach as a unified regulator following the conjoining of SEBI with FMC. That said, the SEBI fetish for always following the arcane rule books of Indian markets led to Samir receiving only a 6 month contract renewal due to Sebi fiat. He will be forced to reapply for his job in an open call if he wishes to stay beyond March 2018.

166 John Griffith-Jones
Chairman
FCA UK

Griffiths-Jones is on the glide path to completing his five year term and has made clear he will depart the FCA in March 2018, as originally agreed in 2013.

167 William Donaldson
Chairman
IEX

The great William Donaldson is as close as they come to a living legend in the parish, alongside the likes of Richard "Doc" Sandor and Leo Melamed. A successful young officer in the Korean war, he founded his eponymous boutique, chaired the SEC and nowadays, amongst a myriad of other achievements is the chairman of IEX. There are many influential people on this list but very few great men. William Donaldson is absolutely one of them.

168 Rabi Narayan Das
Chairman
NCDEX

Rabi Narayan Das is a former chief information commissioner of the Gujarat Information Commission and is now chairman of the National Commodities Derivatives Exchange (NCDEX), India's second largest commodity exchange behind the Multi Commodity Exchange (MCX).

169 Brenda Hoffman
CTO
NASDAQ

Having come from TMX, Brenda Hoffman appears to have made an elegant transition to the complexities of NASDAQ.

170 Ken Griffin
CEO
Citadel

As a multi-billionaire hedge fund founder who has branched out across investment markets, Ken Griffin's leading influence stems from not merely his direct actions trading across markets but in particular his drive to democratise / open up post OTC IRS markets where many legacy banks see the game as 'dealing outside' the platforms with counterparty banks, as opposed to engaging in a free market.

171 Lauri Rosendahl
SVP Europe & President NASDAQ Nordics
NASDAQ
FESE Member of the Board

The man in charge of cash and derivatives markets in NASDAQ Nordics as well as the Stockholm SE directly.

172 Robert Barnes
CEO
Turquoise (LSEG)

From serious physicist to LIFFE floor runner, Robert Barnes has a broad range of experience and his reputation for running equity platforms successfully has been further upgraded with his stewardship of Turquoise following on from his creation of the UBS MTF. Robert first came to prominence for many parishioners with his active input as a leading member of LIBA back in its heyday.

173 David Mercer
CEO
LMAX Exchange

MBO'd from its parent Betfair before the platform could find its feet, the LMAX CEO has a sound track record of promoting reform in the forex dealing industry as well as building an excellent attractive platform.

174 Michael Cole-Fontayn
Chairman EMEA
BNY Mellon
Chairman AFME

As chairman of AFME, Cole-Fontayn has influence over the parish representing banking counterparties and related sell side entities.

175 Peter Reitz
CEO
European Energy Exchange (EEX)
Europex General Assembly

Peter Reitz is perhaps the only DB1 senior exec to have improved his ratings in the past year. He has single-mindedly focussed on EEX and built a significant portfolio of assets including recent acquisitions such as Cleartrade and Nodal Exchange. If a vacancy emerges for DB1 CEO then Reitz is by far the strongest internal candidate based on his pure play execution and growth track record.

176-200

176 Mark Ibbotson
Group CEO
G.H. Financials
FIA Member of the Board

"Ibbo" remains a leading figure in the world of the GCMs and as CEO of GHF is a popular and key player in the ETD industry with a sound experience of the parish having formerly been a longstanding staffer at LIFFE.

177 Lamon Rutten
CEO
ICDX

Lamon has influence in countries across the globe where many parishioners may struggle to find their bearings. Now CEO of ICDX in Indonesia, he was formerly CEO of MCX and before that a leading figure in UNCTAD across the parish.

178 Saurabh Chandra
Chairman
MCX India

After some instability post NSEL/FTIL meltdown MCX is finding its mojo once again with Saurabh Chandra providing a deft touch towards regaining growth.

179 Thomas Book
CEO
Eurex

The EUREX glory days appear long past while the general mojo of DB1 remains in hiatus pending an outbreak of management at the top of the group but Thomas Book steers the EUREX business day to day without incident.

180 Yupawan Sirichainarumitr
The Stock Exchange of Thailand
MD

With Thailand back to something like political stability in the macro, the SET has multiple initiatives in play including for SMEs.

181 Lars Ottersgard
EVP Market Technology
NASDAQ

Lars has had a good couple of years heading up the IT sales arm of NASDAQ.

182 Veronica Augustsson
CEO
Cinnober

The popular CEO of Cinnober has been involved in various transactions including the development of the new bank clearing arm and TradeEcho etc.

183 Peter Randall
CEO
SETL

Peter Randall has, like Blythe Masters, done an admirable job of selling the concept of SETL but the move beyond POC to a tangible vendor is clearly going to be the proof of the business.

184 Blythe Masters
CEO
Digital Asset Holdings

DAH has done a sublime job raising funding but it remains less clear just how the actual rollout of its Blockchain software will go.

185 Michael Völter
Chairman
Boerse Stuttgart

As chairman of Boerse Stuttgart, Michael Voelter oversees an enterprise which remains broadly unknown beyond the German speaking world but is a veritable powerhouse in cash equities, bonds and various derivatives as well as owning the Nordic Growth Market.

186 Sokrates Lazaridis
CEO
Helex

The Hellenic Exchange is unfairly forgotten as the bourse itself is a sound organisation – it's just a pity that the entire Greek nation remains dysfunctional.

187 Gregor Pottmeyer
CFO
DB

With his contract extended in May for another 5 years until 2022, it is feasible Gregor Pottmeyer is one of very few DB1 senior managers to be largely assured of making it back to this listing next year.

188 Chris Corrado
Group COO & CIO
LSEG

Chris Corrado was appointed Group COO and CIO in November 2015, having previously been CIO/CTO of MSCI since 2013. He was once CTO of eBay and at LSE replaced Antoine Shagoury.

189 Sebastian Albella Amigo
Chairman
CNMV
ESMA Management Board

Sebastian Albella Amigo is chairman of Spanish Regulator Comision Nacional del Mercado de Valores (CNMV) and a member of the ESMA Management board.

190 David Weild
Chairman & CEO
Weild & Co

The Father of the JOBS Act, the leading exponent of equity crowdfunding in the USA, David Weild has clear influence in the SME funding domain across not merely North America but the entire world.

191 Leonardo P. Gomes Pereira
Chairman
Comissao de Valores Mobiliarios
IOSCO Member of the Board

The chairman of the Brazilian regulator is also a member of the IOSCO board.

192 Takamichi Hamada
President & CEO
TOCOM

With product launches in gold oil and platinum to name but three in the past year alone, TOCOM is pushing forward on multiple fronts.

193 Klaus Kumpfmuller
Executive Director
FMA
ESMA Management Board

Austrian Klaus Kumpfmuller is Executive Director of the Austrian Financial Market Authority (FMA), a member of the board of supervisors and of the management board of ESMA and a member of the Single Resolution Board (SRB).

194 Raffaele Jerusalmi
CEO
Borsa Italiana (LSEG)

The head of Borsa Italiana has profited handsomely from the LSE takeover and continues to run the Milan arm of the LSE business as well as being in charge of capital markets and sitting on the LSE board.

195 David Hardy
GCSA
Chairman

The former LCH CEO who masterminded the acquisition of Clearnet still receives less than his fair share of plaudits for being the man who championed SwapClear, RepoClear and indeed just about any other noun appended to the stem "-clear" during an era when LCH built the foundations which it has been able to leverage since the Lehman collapse. Nowadays assiduous in his work for better CCP practices behind the scenes as Chairman of GCSA, David has several interesting involvements which look to be gaining traction in areas with tricky problems requiring considered solutions.

196 Kostas Pantazopoulos
MD
Goldman Sachs
AFME Vice-Chairman

AFME Vice Chairman from Goldman Sachs, influential based on the corporate names alone.

197 Martin Watkins
EMEIA Lead for Exchanges & FMIs
EY
Board Member CISI

In the background everywhere it seems from LBMA to Astana, and many other parts beside, Martyn Watkins maintains a profile which EY would struggle to retain without his vast contact list obtained through several decades of considerable experience in various positions amid all elements of the market structure, particularly in derivatives and CCPs.

198 Yim Jong-yong
Chairman
FSC
IOSCO Member of the Board

Yim Jongyong runs the FSC which directs the FSS. He shares the South Korean IOSCO board position with Zhin Woong-Seob:

199 Zhin Woong-Seob
Governor
FSS
IOSCO Member of the Board

The Governor of the South Korean regulator and member of the IOSCO board, Zhin Woon-Seob became FSC Governor after the departure due to a scandal of Choi Soo-hyun. It is unclear how long any of the current regulators will survive in the rather febrile South Korean political milieu at the time of going to press in the wake of the Presidential impeachment.

200 Chong Kim Seng
CEO of derivatives
Bursa Malaysia

Heads the Bursa Malaysia derivatives subsidiary.

201-225

201 Colin Heffron
CEO
GFI Group

The GFI CEO stayed on following the BGC acquisition.

202 George Handjinicolaou
Deputy CEO Head of EMEA
ISDA
Chairman of Piraeus Bank

George Handjinicolaou, a former fixed income trader at Dresdner Kleinwort Benson, Bank of America Merrill Lynch has also been Chairman of Piraeus Bank since November 2016 as well as Deputy CEO and Head of Europe, Middle East and Africa for ISDA.

203 Andrea Pignataro
CEO & Founder
ION

Another very low profile figure who, through owning a great deal of the plumbing outside the execution of ETD in particular, has remarkable parish influence.

204 Haywood Cheung
President
Chinese Gold and Silver Exchange Society

The Chinese Gold and Silver Exchange Society (CGSE) is notably coop-erating with HKEX following an agreement signed in June 2017.

205 Conny Anderson
SVP Clearing & Nordic Markets
NASDAQ

A longstanding OMX-NASDAQ manager, Conny oversees the development, delivery and support of the Nordic and Baltic market systems including the systems used for Equity and fixed income trading, derivatives trading and clearing, Nordic Central Counterparty (CCP) post-trade infrastructure, market data, and back-office services. Additionally, he oversees the coordination of Nordic IT initiatives and the development and support of clearing solutions to Nasdaq Market Technology customers.

206 Tan Sri Amirsham Bin A Aziz
Chairman
Bursa Malaysia

Tan Sri Amirsham Bin A Aziz was appointed chairman of Bursa Malaysia succeeding Tun Mohamed Dzaiddin Haji Abdullah on March 1st 2015. He is also chairman of Malaysian Investment Development Authority (MIDA).

207 Daniel J Davies
GC
CFTC

Appointed General Counsel of the CFTC, in March 2017, joining from Proskauer Rose LLP, where he was Special Counsel in the Labor & Employment Law Department.

208 Oscar N. Onyema
CEO
Nigerian Stock Exchange
President ASEA

The CEO of the Nigerian Stock Exchange is one of the most passionate proponents of his national market and is working hard to secure not merely the listing of NSE but also a much broader and more successful Nigerian SE. He also presides over the African Exchanges body, ASEA. Formerly Onyema was SVP and Chief Administrative Officer at the AMEX, playing a key role in integrating the exchange into the NYSE Euronext business which acquired AMEX in 2008.

209 Hiroki Tsuda
Chairman
JPX

Hiroki Tsuda, a former deputy finance minister, became chairman of the JPX board of directors, succeeding Masakazu Hayashi in April 2015.

210 Nikolaos Porfyris
Deputy COO
Helex
ECSDA Executive Committee member

Nikos Porfyris is active in FESE as vice of the Management Committee, an executive committee member of ECSDA and strongly involved in the management of various elements of the Greek Stock Exchange where he has worked since 1998.

211 Mohammed Al-Jadaan
Chairman
CMA

The Chairman of the Saudi Arabian regulator is a former member of the IOSCO board.

212 Xu Zhen
Chairman
Shanghai Clearing House

As chairman of Shanghai Clearing House, which oversees a major part of China's interbank bond market Xu Zhen has been vocal in the past year not merely promoting the Shanghai-HK Bond Connect as only the beginning of more such projects but also investigating the potential for links to major western CCPs including CME, EUREX, LCH et al.

213 Eleni Gabre-Madhin
CEO
Eleni

Eleni Gabre-Madhin came to prominence as the founder of the Ethiopian Commodity Exchange and has since gone on to create Eleni LLC which seeks to add value across the African continent.

214 Rene Karsenti
President
ICMA

ICMA President (former CEO) Rene Karsenti is a veteran of the bond markets and has pretty much anybody who is anybody on his speed dial.

215 Christopher Edmonds
SVP
Financial Markets
ICE

Chris Edmonds oversees development of initiatives within ICE's exchange listed and OTC financial markets, including all futures and options, credit derivatives, ICE Link and ICE Swap Trade. In some rival exchanges they would probably need a battalion of SVPs to achieve the same oversight.

216 Michael Aitken
CEO & Chief Scientist
Capital Markets CRC

Winning the Prime Minister's Prize for Innovation in his native Australia was just the icing on the cake for Michael Aitken who has been a pioneer of so many efforts to drive transparency into markets from all angles (including SMARTS, the surveillance system he created and sold to NASDAQ). At the cutting edge of market thinking, Professor Mike is a huge benefit to the parish while his ambitions now expand beyond just the CMCRC into other areas of big data.

217 Apurv Bagri
Non-Executive Director
HKEX

Member of the legendary LME Bagri dynasty, he bagged a seat on the HKEX parent board in 2016 while also running the family MetDist metals business. Sadly his father Raj passed away this past year.

218 Peter Jessup
EVP
NASDAQ

Peter Jessup is senior vice president of Global Software Development and Head of Development for Market Technology Systems at NASDAQ, based in Sydney. One of the original X-stream team, Peter has an memory of market technology to back up his brilliant innovative brain.

219 Juan Pablo Cordoba
CEO
BVC
Member of the WFE Board

The Colombian bourse CEO was a one term compromise candidate WFE chairman during one of that organisation's periodic inabilities to progress. Still a WFE board member but maintaining a lower profile.

220 Leo Melamed
Chairman Emeritus & NED
CME

Leo Melamed has been diligently involved with initiatives in China for some years now albeit the concern must be that the Duffy era seems to be more focussed on the domestic product base.

221 Diana Chan
CEO
EuroCCP

At the epicentre of much of the EU's equity CCP business, Diana is a high profile and eloquent participant in industry discussions.

222 Pan Gongsheng
Head of the State Administration of Foreign Exchange
Government of China

Pan Gongsheng, head of the State Administration of Foreign Exchange is mulling more ways to enhance the onshore bond market now that Bond Connect is up and running.

223 Hiromi Yamaji
President &
CEO
Osaka Securities Exchange

Subsumed into JPX as part of the Tokyo merger of 2013, Osaka SE has origins dating back to 1878 and is the home to Nikkei futures.

224 Godfried De Vidts
Director of European Affairs
NEX
Member of the Board ECMI & ICMA

Godfried De Vidts stayed with NEX when the ICAP deal happened and it is understandable why Michael Spencer was eager to keep hold of his talents. Asides from running NEX's presence in Brussels, Godfried is also an ICMA and ECMI board member.

225 Lee Boon Ngiap
Assistant MD & Head of Capital Markets
MAS
IOSCO Member of the Board

The MAS retains significant clout both in the progressive City state and all the way around the world.

226-250

226 Iwona Sroka
CEO
KDPW
ECSDA Executive Committee member

Away from the often chaotic soap opera which has engulfed the politically charged Warsaw Stock Exchange, Iwona Sroka maintains an orderly presence running the entirely government owned KDPW which has morphed from a CSD into a fully-fledged CCP with major operations not only in Polish Zloty interest rates (albeit LCH still leads in the sector) but also energy markets thanks to the success of the Polish energy exchange TGE/PolPX.

227 Jean-Paul Servais
Chairman
Financial Services & Markets Authority Belgium
IOSCO Vice-Chairman

The leading regulator of Belgium is also on the board of IOSCO.

228 Ranjit Ajit Singh
Chairman
SEC Malaysia
IOSCO Vice-Chairman

IOSCO vice chairman and chairman of the Malaysian regulator.

229 Craig Heimark
NED
DB

Craig Heimark habitually relieves any room of one elemental task when he enters – the role of who possesses the most raw intellect almost invariably falls to him. A clear thinker, born of the infamous O'Connor partnership which propelled SBC then UBS forward in a myriad of trading activities, Craig has a sensational Rolodex from his years at the cutting edge of financial technology way before the 'kids' got into this bubble called fintech. Heimark is a great man and it is to be hoped he can help DB1 make progress to recover from the epic failure of the Merger of Equal Desperation.

230 Thomas Schaefer
Finance Minister
Hesse State Government

The man who explicitly noted that Hesse (and perhaps even Germany) does not welcome corporate attraction from the US. His epic line came as the burning carcass of the Merger of Equal Desperation between DB1 and LSE was still being hosed down by fire-fighters in late March. "Deutsche Boerse is not only a private company but it also has state responsibilities," Thomas Schaefer, finance minister for the German state of Hesse, told reporters.

"The stock exchange authorities of Germany have to guarantee that if there is a change of owner, it has to guarantee that business has to continue uninterrupted as normal and it doesn't matter who makes an offer", and when it came to explicitly American intentions, he added: "I would rather recommend colleagues in America not to attempt to do this". Thus highly influential in closing off the potential US deal that had been discussed in the past with the likes of CME as well as hopefully helping DB1 to focus its attentions on internal restructuring as opposed to the casino capitalist approach of seeking to keep merging with a leading player beyond the European mainland as has plagued DB1 'thinking' for a decade or more.

231 Nicolas Bertrand
Head of Equity & Derivatives Markets
LSE

Frenchman who came of age working for Borsa Italiana and then relocated to London in time for the rise of Xavier Rolet. Good product brain, good understanding of the Anglo Saxon paradigm as well as both French and Italian approaches to commerce.

232 Allan Malvar
MD Head of Membership & Communications
ICMA

Allan Malvar is simply the most brilliant organiser I have ever seen in the parish. His colleagues have been known to marvel at his ability to organise major ICMA fora without breaking a sweat. In an era of poor execution, Allan manages to maintain a firm grip on PR and Comms for ICMA as well as effortlessly managing ICMA's events large and small all over the world.

233 Patrick Pearson
Head of financial markets structure
EC

The EC's Head of Financial Market Structure is doubtless a tad tetchy about Brexit but also has overseen a welter of regulation in recent years which has affected every aspect of the parish.

234 Trabue Bland
President
ICE Futures US

Tribe Bland was elevated from VP Regulation to running the ICE Futures US business in 2016, Trabue has been with ICE for a decade, joining in 2007 after he served as Counsel to then CFTC Acting Chairman Walt Lukken (now the boss of the FIA).

235 Kenneth E. Bentsen, Jr.
President & CEO
SIFMA

The former Congressman for Texas and nephew of Treasury Secretary Lloyd Bentson, Kenneth E Bentson Jr was named Chairman of the Financial Services Industry's Engage China Coalition in 2016 in addition to his role as president and CEO of SIFMA.

236 Mayur Kapani
CTO
ICE

Probably very unfairly treated to be so low in the influence stack, Mayur Kapani may have a relatively low profile (as is not uncommon amongst many ICE executives) but his role as CTO for the $38 billion company makes him highly significant in the parish. Technology pedigree dates back to working at the PHLX, Mayur has been with ICE since 2006.

237 Ken Pigaga
Global COO
NEX

While it appeared at first Pigaga would head over to TP with the voice assets of ICAP, it subsequently became clear he was remaining in some sense a chattel of the house of Spencer and as such was installed as Global COO of NEX Group early in 2017.

238 Daniel Marcus
CEO
ParFX Tradition

Runs ParFX (transparent fx platform) initiative as well as occupying the role of Global Head of Strategy and Business Development for ParFX's parent company Tradition.

239 Sunil Cutinho
President
CME Clearing

Marking his 15th year with CME Group, Sunil has been immersed in the CCP throughout this time, rising to becoming a popular and respected president of the Clearing House.

240 Ulf Axman
Head of Sales
Cinnober

One of lowest profile figures in the list, Ulf Axman has rarely been far from any major technology deal in the parish during the past twenty years, repeatedly on the successful side of the equation with several different vendors before reaching what some might see as a spiritual home in Cinnober.

241 Hauke Stars
Executive Board Member
DB

DB1 is trying hard in its cash market and particularly its SME funding approaches, now that it seems to have finally got over its longstanding trauma of NeuerMarkt. Whether DB1 can be relied upon to go full circle with their SME funding initiatives remains to be seen but Hauke Stars is a capable executive to lead such initiatives (her job title officially states she is "responsible for Cash Market, Pre-IPO & Growth Financing" – albeit she too may decide to preserve her career as opposed to risking the German media wrath if the market turns down).

242 Lou Eccleston
CEO
TMX

"What's the really long term business plan for how these businesses work together? That's what doesn't normally get articulated...I think if the next [merger] starts with that, it might have a better chance." Despite a single insightful comment on mergers, Eccleston is not making a huge mark on the global or even local scene despite there being considerable talent within the organisation. Given his low profile, he ranks significantly below what we would anticipate for the TMX CEO to find a 'natural' level of influence.

243 Anthony Attia
Global Head of Listing, CEO Euronext Paris
Euronext

The CEO of Euronext Paris is also globally in charge of listing at Euronext, a business which has seen some strong traction for IPOs in the past year.

244 John P. Davidson
COO
OCC

Moving from being Chief Compliance Officer of Citigroup to working for Craig Donohue at OCC, John P. Davidson was appointed to the high profile role of president and COO as the former CME CEO Donohue fundamentally re-engineers the OCC.

245 Julie Holzrichter
COO
CME Group

Low profile compared to the rest of the team but keeps busy in the COO role for the diverse CME global operations which she has occupied since 2014.

246 H.E. Sheik Ahmed Bin Jassim Bin Mohammed Al-Thani
Minister of Economy & Commerce Chairman
Qatar Stock Exchange

The chairman of the Qatar SE is also the Minister of Economy and Commerce.

247 Dhirendra Swarup
Chairman
BSE India

Dhirenda Swarup is a former Chairman of Pension Funds Regulatory and Development Authority and has over four decades of experience in the Indian civil service. He was an independent non-executive director of BSE before being appointed chairman in August 2017.

248 Marc-Robert Nicoud
CEO (holding and international)
Clearstream

Marc-Robert Nicoud was given the joint custody of Clearstream alongside Philip Brown when Jeff Tessler was elevated to run EUREX after Carsten Kengeter was appointed CEO of Deutsche Boerse in 2015.

249 Stuart Irving
CEO
Computershare

With its multiplicity of services in and around the registry business, Computershare retains significant clout world wide from its HQ in Australia.

250 Mathias Papenfuss
CEO
Clearstream Services
Chairman of ECSDA

251-275

251 Philip Brown
Co-CEO
Clearstream Banking

Co-CEO of Clearstream Banking SA with Philippe Seyll.

252 Philippe Seyll
Co-CEO
Clearstream Banking

Co-CEO with Philip Brown of Clearstream Banking.

253 Paul Hamill
Global Head of FICC
Citadel

Responsible for the client facing FICC business at Citadel, Hamil is in one of the positions which most infuriates the old cartel of banks endeavouring to keep newcomers out of the old bilateral fiefdoms.

254 Richard M. McVey
Chairman & CEO
MarketAxess

As the founder, chairman and CEO of MarketAxess, Richard McVey keeps a relatively low profile in the style of the more old line brokers but his business has massive clout across the globe.

255 Billy Hult
President
Tradeweb

Coming up on a decade at Tradeweb, like CEO Lee Olesky, Billy Hult has a skill of being both fast when innovation is required and patient when the Bond market is trying to catch up.

256 Khalid Abdullah Al Hussan
CEO
Tadawul

Khalid Abdullah Al Hussan has been with Tadawul since 2007 having previously worked in insurance. He has been proactive in the recent past as he seeks to modernise the Saudi stock exchange.

257 Stanislav Ivanov
President
ICE Clear Credit & TCC

Stan Ivanov is president of ICE Clear Credit, one of ICE's wholly-owned clearing houses. Ivanov was instrumental to the launch of the CDS clearing services at ICE Trust US and ICE Clear Europe in 2009 while earlier in his career before he joined ICE, he was the architect of OCC's risk management approach known as the System for Theoretical Analysis and Numerical Simulations (STANS).

258 Erik Tim Muller
CEO
Eurex Clearing

259 Gedon Herschten
Founder & Chairman
Hertshten Group

A parish veteran who began on the CBOT floor in 1978, Gedon was a director of LIFFE from 1997 to 2005 and retains the majority of GHF which has a foothold in derivatives trading and clearing across the globe.

260 Sarah Al-Suhaimi
Chairman
Tadawul

Sarah Al-Suhaimi who became the first female chief executive of a Saudi investment bank when she took on the role at NBC Capital in 2014, accepted the offer to chair Saudi Arabia's Tadawul, the largest bourse in the Middle East, replacing Khalid Al Rabiah, in mid-February.

261 M. Clark Hutchison
MD
Deutsche Bank Securities Inc
FIA Treasurer, Member of the Board

The Deutsche Bank staffer is an FIA board member and serves as treasurer.

262 Nikhil Rathi
CEO LSE & Director of International Development
LSEG

Little known fact: the man currently in charge of the London Stock Exchange segment of LSE Group, Nikhil Rathi, served as Private Secretary to the UK Prime Minister for three years from 2005 to 2008 (the bit where the spendthrift Gordon Brown was bankrupting Britain, essentially). Nowadays Nikhil Rathi also has responsibility for international development amidst the broad ambitions of the LSE Group across the globe.

263 Nonkululeko Nyembezi-Heita
Chairman
Johannesburg Stock Exchange

Nonkululeko Nyembezi-Heita was appointed chairman of JSE in 2013, which leaves Johannesburg as one of the few exchanges alongside Oslo, for instance, with both a woman chairman and a woman CEO. Her background is in steel, telecoms and finance and she has been CEO since 2014 of Dutch mining group, IchorCoal N.V.

264 Hamad Abdulla Al Shamsi
Chairman
Abu Dhabi Securities Exchange

Hamad Abdulla Al Shamsi has a broad portfolio of directorships and interests in the Emirates as well as being chairman of ADX.

265 Hassan Abdulrahman Al Serkal
COO
Dubai Financial Market

Hassan Abdulrahman Al Serkal began his career in telecoms before moving to join the startup phase at DFM in 1998.

266 Jerre Stead
Chairman & CEO
IHS Markit

Jerre Stead, originally a reluctant CEO of IHS, is now keeping the overall CEO position of IHS Markit warm for Lance Uggla with Stead looking unlikely to stay on much longer with his 75th birthday beckoning.

267 Christian Martin
CEO & Co-Founder
TeraExchange

As well as running Tera Exchange which he cofounded, Christian sits on the board of the Wall Street Blockchain Alliance.

268 Gerben J. Everts
AFM Board Member
IOSCO Member of the Board

Board member of the Dutch regulator AFM and board member of IOSCO.

269 Tim Grange
Director of Regulatory Policy
ICE Futures Europe
EACH & FESE Member of the Board

Tim Grange remains a clear value-focussed thinker who delivers results in the classic ICE management mode. He is a very useful addition to both the boards of EACH and FESE.

270 Bente A. Landsnes
President & CEO Oslo Bors
Chairman Fish Pool, FESE Member of the Board

Bente retains a clear understanding of Oslo's unique positioning on the edge of the EU alongside Norway's interesting, independent marketplace which has much value amidst a remarkable economy.

271 Markus Ferber
Deputy Chairman of ECON committee
EuroParl

Markus Ferber is a veteran career MEP who knows the levers of the Econ committee perhaps better than anybody. His influence on financial markets can be toxic as he endeavours to raise his popularity, having been superseded within the Christian Social Union (CSU) party's European leadership after a poor 2014 EuroParl election process. Nevertheless, whether he is politicking, grandstanding or working on yet more regulation, Ferber has the influence of his longstanding tenure in Brussels.

272 Lex Hoogduin
Group Chairman
LCH

The group chairman of LCH, has, since the historic UK Brexit vote, managed to broadly leave the Euro derivatives politicking to his executive team, at least in public.

273 Jaime Caruana
GM
BIS

As we close for press, former Bank of Spain Governor Jaime Caruana has been in situ somewhat beyond the originally mandated extension to his expanded term as BIS GM which was due to expire in March 2017.

274 Seth Merrin
CEO & Founder
Liquidnet

Seth Merrin remains one of the clearest thinkers in the market on his good days. Liquidnet remains the 500lb gorilla of block equity trading and is making healthy inroads in bond markets too.

275 Fredrik Ekstrom
Head of Nordic Fixed Income & Clearing
NASDAQ

Fredrik Ekstrom has been having a good run in recent times. A considered thinker, he runs the CCP which is dwarfed by the big three in Europe but maintains a significant niche position dominating clearing in the Nordic region.

276-300

276 Minder Cheng
Chairman
ITG

Minder Cheng was appointed on the back of investor lobbying to help clear house at ITG alongside new CEO Frank Troise in Q1 2016.

277 Jim Bird
President & CTO
BIDS Trading

As the man running the BIDS technology, which is not only delivering great work in the US but also the stunningly successful from scratch nascent LiS with BATS in Europe, Jim Bird has had a busy year.

278 Barney Reynolds
Head of GFI Advisory & Financial Regulatory Group & Global Co-Head of FI
Shearman & Sterling

Barney Reynolds is one of the leading thinkers in the Brexit space who has advised many of the leading exchanges and CCPs over the years. Has significant influence across the Atlantic as well as playing a key role in shaping thinking for post-Brexit Britain through the ground-breaking Prosperity UK conference bringing together Remainers and Brexiteers to shape the future of Britain, and the world, trade and markets.

279= Peter Lenardos
MD
RBC Capital Markets

Peter Lenardos has carved out a remarkable reputation across the parish – the only convincingly trans-Atlantic analyst in the publicly quoted space Peter maintains a remarkable Rolodex of exchange staff and investors not to mention being a favourite of the World Federation of Exchanges.

279= Rich Repetto
Principal Equity Research
Sandler O'Neill & Partners

Rich Repetto is perhaps the leading name in the analysis of the US public stocks in the parish. As such, his position as number one in the queue at the analyst calls is broadly assured. Rarely seen outside his New York habitat, he has clout with a few key names in the industry but in the broader parish he is barely known.

280= Russ Behnam
280= Brian Quintenz
Commissioners
CFTC

Messrs Quintenz & Behnam caused an 11th hour shakeup in the rankings thanks to their being approved by the Senate as Commissioners of the CFTC in early August just as this list was heading to press.

281 Dan Maguire
Group COO
LCH

Dan Maguire is one of the figures at LCH who receives high praise from all quarters. He has the capacity to help push the London Clearing House enterprise forward.

282 Roberto Gualtieri
Chairman of ECON Committee
EuroParl

The Econ committee may be part of a Parliament which often looks more like a student body so incoherent are the economics of the EuroParl's decisions but Chairing the Econ committee gives MEP Gualtieri serious clout in parish affairs from the EU to the world.

283 Jaime Gonzalez Aguade
President
CNBV
IOSCO Member of the Board

The leading Mexican regulator is also on the board of IOSCO.

284 Michael Davie
Global Head of Rates
LCH

Michael has recently rejoined LCH after more than 18 months as Head of Rates Services at LSEG, developing the Group's approach to rates products and overseeing the launch of CurveGlobal where Michael retains the post of chairman.

285 Artur Fischer
Joint CEO
Boerse Berlin

Artur has a strong history of cutting edge technological innovation streaming through his veins and he maintains that intriguing niche, the Berlin Stock Exchange, as well as being a well-known figure on the conference circuit and in the media, discussing markets and European affairs. A sound parish thinker with a strong Europhile streak.

286 Alasdair Haynes
CEO
Aquis Exchange

Few manage such a high profile in London and remain so sought after as speakers as does Alasdair Haynes with his many insights in all forms of markets. Originally from the derivatives end of the parish, it is in cash markets, first of all with ITG, that he has become most known. His latest "all you can eat" platform Aquis has not achieved dizzy volumes but Alasdair's conviction remains high while he has managed some useful technology sales of his platform to help boost the bottom line.

287 Christoph Landis
CEO
Swiss Exchange

Heads the Swiss Exchange side of the SiX group with positive Swiss reserve.

288 Tarek Al-Wazir
Economics Minister
Hesse State Government

Given that German politics has been largely left leaning for a decade and more, Tarek Al-Wazir is a Green party Finance Minister for Hesse so his pro-market credentials are hardly plausible. At the same time, his utterances have made more logic than many in the infantile magic money tree atmosphere engendered by Angela Merkel's broad fiscal sclerosis across the nation. Born to a Yemeni father and German Mother, Tarek Al-Wazir holds parish influence this year for his role in the Merger of Equal Desperation where he was essentially as protectionist as the other Germans politicians in the mix. Has ongoing relevance as he remains naively bullish that the Euro derivatives market will somehow or other overcome the manifest issues of Eurozone financial centres to see Hesse triumph against the powerful incumbency of LCH and its 17 Euro offsets.

289 Rinjai Chakornpipat
Senior EVP
The Stock Exchange of Thailand

Senior EVP at SET who also oversees the derivatives business.

290 David Morgan
Chairman
CHi-X Australia

"This place is ripe for innovation. It is the 20th largest economy in the world, but the fourth or fifth largest pension system in the world and it is chronically undiversified." A stellar CV (former CEO of Westpac, current exec chairman for Asia and Europe of Chi-X owner JC Flowers) accompanied by a direct execution style, has tweaked the direction of Chi-X Australia since he became chairman in 2016.

291 Rupert Robson
Chairman
TP ICAP

As chairman of TP ICAP, Rupert Robson is in a fascinating position helping to steer the work of "Phiz" and team to create a silk purse from a lot of pigs' ears... NB Used to be a director of LME.

292 Jean Desgagne
President & CEO Global Enterprise Services
TMX

Jean Desgagne remains a key thinker within the TMX organisation, who pays close attention to the world far beyond the confines of both Bay Street and Quebec. He was deservedly promoted from President and CEO Global Enterprise Services just as the EI1000 closed for press to the newly created position of President & CEO TMX Global Solutions, Insights & Analytics Strategies, reporting directly to CEO Lou Eccleston.

293 Thomas J. Curry
Comptroller of the Currency
US Government

Arguably influential not just in the greenback but perhaps more significantly in how the US adjusts to cryptocurrency.

294 John F. W. Rogers
EVP Chief Of Staff & Secretary To The Board
Goldman Sachs
GFMA & SIFMA Board Member

A Goldman Sachs big cheese who is the eyes and ears of Lloyd Blankfein on the GFMA & SIFMA boards.

295 Glenn Goucher
President CDS & CDCC
TMX

Until recently playing an influential role in the world's CCP movement via CCP12 and the American CSD association, Glenn remains a clear thinker from the old Montreal Exchange management team now within the larger TMX structure.

296 Rob Park
CTO
IEX Group

Driving the technology either side of and right through the infamous speed bump, Rob has extensive HFT and algo experience which has allowed him to think about market structure in his IEX role.

297 Richard Leung
Deputy CIO
HKEX

Given the key brief to consolidate oversight of IT management and platform development across HKEX group as part of an HKEX restructuring in June 2017.

298 Glenn Lesko
President & CEO
Bloomberg Tradebook

Having moved from Instinet to run Bloomberg Tradebook, Glenn Lesko is trying to leverage the awesome data computational power of the Bloomberg platform as he seeks to broaden and deepen the execution power of the Tradebook platform.

299 Nick Themelis
CIO
MarketAxess

CIO since 2005, Themelis is a key player in the explosive growth of MarketAxess and the Open Trading protocol nurtured by Nick since 2012 is a key component of recent growth.

300 Stacey Cunningham
COO
NYSE

An accomplished chef with a lengthy involvement in NYSE, Cunningham ably supports President Tom Farley as the ICE remakes a modern NYSE.

301-325

301 Jay Spencer
CIO
Tradeweb

A genuine electronic trading pioneer, Jay Spencer will celebrate his 10th year as Tradeweb CIO in 2018, where he reunited with CEO Lee Olesky, having been the founding CTO at Brokertec.

302 Hans B. Sicat
Chief Integration Officer
The Philippine Stock Exchange

The former CEO of the PSE Hans Sicat is now overseeing the merger (a longstanding saga in its gestation akin to a telenovela) with the PDS bond platform which he architected. He will depart the parish soon after this tome is published to become the country manager of ING Bank.

303 Svein Andresen
Secretary General
Financial Stability Board (FSB)

With the FSF since its inception in 1999, Svein Andresen moved to the same position of Secretary General with the FSB when it was established in 2009

304 Martin Reck
MD Cash Markets
DB
FESE Member of the Board

Martin Reck is DB1 cash markets MD who is capable of seeing beyond the sometimes parochial Frankfurt worldview. Plays an active constructive role in FESE.

305 Michael Peters
Deputy CEO
Eurex
ICDA Member of the Board

The Deputy CEO of EUREX also holds a board position with ICDA (the former Swiss Futures & Options Association).

306 Thomas P. Gallagher
Chairman & CEO
MIAX Options

Attorney Thomas P. Gallagher has headed the MIAX team since foundation, driving the building of a consortium of key users for both MIAX Options and MIAX PEARL.

307 Himmet Karadag
Chairman
Borsa Istanbul

BIST had another reshuffle this year after a traumatic year for Turkey and even a spate of arrests of former staff who were deemed to be supportive of opposition leader in exile, Fethullah Gulen. Himmet Karadağ has been chairman of Borsa Istanbul since 2016 and was appointed as director of the Turkish (Sovereign) Wealth Fund when it was established in January 2017 with BIST as a core element of the SWF portfolio.

308 Brian Taylor
CEO
BTA

One of the most influential technologists/managers behind the scenes in the industry across the world and the full technology stack.

309 Lowri Evans
Director General
EC Markets

Lowri Evans has been EC director-general of the Directorate-General for Internal Market, Industry, Entrepreneurship and SMEs since September 2015 and thus is significant to the parish as, if the EU can deliver a coherent Capital Markets Union, her department will play a key role in at least the SME end of the equation.

310 Uwe Schweickert
Director
EUREX
FESE Member of the Board

Uwe Schweickert serves as a FESE Board member as well as being a director of EUREX Frankfurt.

311 Brian Healy
Director of Traded Markets, Development, Operations
Irish Stock Exchange

Probably one of the most knowledgeable executives in the exchange world anywhere, Brian remains well informed across all product classes, even far beyond the breadth of the ISE offering.

312 Fredrik Voss
Blockchain guru
NASDAQ

Fredrik has been the NASDAQ Blockchain guru for longer than most folks have even been talking up the distributed ledger. The DL growth process itself has been at its slowest, a development to measure in dog years. A capable executive who has helped shape the NASDAQ offering leaving it with coherent business lines where others are often merely POCs.

313 Heike Eckert
Deputy CEO
Eurex Clearing

Heike Eckert once headed up the Chicago office of EUREX.

314 Benedicte Schilbred Fasmer
Chairman
Oslo Bors

Benedicte Schilbred Fasmer heads up one of the other rare all female chairman/CEO pairings in the parish similar to Johannesburg SE.

315 Oliver Haderup
Chief Compliance Officer
EUREX clearing
Vice Chair of EACH, Vice Chair of CCP12

As deputy chairman of both CCP12 and EACH Oliver maintains considerable influence alongside his executive responsibilities with EUREX.

316 Rick Beaman
CEO
NFX

Appropriately based in Houston, Texas, Rick Beaman runs the NFX which was deftly repurposed as a competing platform for US-oriented energy futures during Hans-Ole Jochumsen's time based in the USA.

317 Tim Cartledge
Chief Strategy Officer
EBS BrokerTec (NEX)

Tim was appointed Global Head of FX and Head of Product for NEX Markets in February 2017, having previously been Chief Strategy Officer of EBS BrokerTec and, prior to that, Head of Global Fixed Income Currencies and Commodities Electronic Trading at Barclays Bank and managing director at Barclays Capital. A key player in the new NEX marketplace network.

318 Masaki Takeda
President & CEO
Nagoya Stock Exchange

Oversees a market of 293 listings of which 73 are exclusive to the exchange which was founded in 1949.

319 Maureen Jensen
Chairman & CEO
Ontario Securities Commission
IOSCO Member of the Board

Chairman and CEO of the Ontario Securities Commission as well as an IOSCO Board member.

320 Corentine Poilvet
Head of Regulatory Strategy & Post Trade Europe
LSEG
Vice Chair of EACH

A lively and engaging figure in the regulatory nexus, Corentine Poilvet is Head of Regulatory Strategy & Post Trade Europe for LSEG and vice chairman of EACH.

321 Rumi Morales
CEO
CME Ventures

Looking for the next gen revolutionary factors to progress a new quantum at CME, Rumi has a huge focus on a big data universe way beyond the average responsibility of most parish execs.

322 Sandy Broderick
Chairman
London DX (LDX)

Industry veteran Sandy Broderick is a strong chairman of the London DX which continues to develop some fascinating methodologies for swap futurisation.

323 Udai Kumar
MD & CEO
MSEI

Udai Kumar replaced Saurabh Sarkar as MSEI CEO permanently in February 2016 after a spell as interim CEO from late 2015. Kumar continues to seek to give the MSEI impetus after various issues, including some SEBI edicts which appeared to sap currency future volume during Sarkar's spell as MD and CEO.

324 Han Chen
Co-CEO
CEINEX

Han Chen is Co-CEO of the Sino-DB1 JV CEINEX.

325 Steve Gibson
CEO
Euclid Opportunities (NEX)

Steve Gibson co-CEOs the EUCLID opportunities fund within NEX. The next year will be interesting to see how tangible the EUCLID portfolio can render any results.

326-350

326 Nick Ogurtsov
COO & Chief Risk Officer
KCG Holdings, Inc.
Member of the Board, DTCC

327 Doug Shulman
EVP Global Head of Client Service Delivery
BNY Mellon
Member of the Board, DTCC

328 Ashwin Kumar
Group Head of Business & Product Development
DB

The head of group product development, there is a golden opportunity for new markets but clearly the size and relative inability of the modern slow-moving DB1 oil tanker to actually innovate may preclude Ashwin Kumar from delivering the opportunities he can see around him.

329 Sergei Poliakoff
CIO
Moscow Exchange

An excellent technology team at MOEX is neatly rounded out by Sergei Poliakoff and his considerable experience gleaned in the New York banking and tech vendor scene before he moved to MOEX.

330 Scott Gordon
Chairman & CEO
Rosenthal Collins Group

A former chairman of CME Group who truly set the revolution in place that has delivered the modern powerhouse, Scott has little direct involvement with the exchange universe but remains an influential figure through his position as a leading independent FCM boss at the almost legendary RCG.

331 Lee Betsill
Chief Risk Officer
CME

The Chief Risk Officer of CME retains a key position albeit with a fewer titles now that the CME Europe regulated entities of CCP and exchange have been closed down.

332 V. Balasubramaniam
CEO
India INX

Brought in to run the BSE subsidiary exchange in Gift City, the project is operative albeit at far too early a stage to make any judgement on its proficiency.

333 Paul Cusenza
Chairman & CEO
Nodal Exchange

Paul Cusenza continues to run Nodal Exchange after it was bought by EEX, the progressive, and somewhat trailblazing arm of DB1 group run by Peter Reitz, earlier in 2017.

334 Ravi Narain
Former Vice-Chairman MD & CEO
NSE India

Still influential despite his resignation from NSE, having hugely shaped that business – a man on the top of many foreigners Rolodex to call when you want to discuss India. It will be interesting to see where Ravi lands post his lengthy period with NSE.

335 Patrick Birley
CEO
NexExchange

Patrick Birley has traversed the gamut of derivatives markets, as SAFEX CEO to the European boss of Doc Sandor's climate exchange as well as leading the LCH end of LCH Clearnet. Now in the fascinating position of re-engineering both the SME exchange world and more specifically what was once ISDX but is now a very different animal as NEXExchange under the watchful gaze of its founder Michael Spencer.

336 Greg Wojciechowski
President & CEO
Bermuda Stock Exchange
Member of the WFE Board

Greg "Wojo" is increasingly a leading figure in all aspects of the Bermudian business community (he joined the board of the Bermuda Business Development Agency in Q2 2017). He also sits on the board of WFE.

337 Louis Morisset
President & CEO
AMF Quebec
IOSCO Member of the Board

Heads the Quebec regulatory organisation and is a member of the IOSCO board.

338 Ian Cornwall
Director, Head of Market Structure
SIX Swiss Exchange
FESE Member of the Board

Active on the FESE board and a leading figure in the Swiss approach to market structure.

339 Guy Debelle
Deputy Governor
RBA

The chair of the BIS working group for developing the forex code of conduct, Debelle produced a competent report albeit one which probably stopped short of getting the forex movement out of the regulatory woods, as it stuck with the antiquated 'last look' provision.

340 Erik Thedeen
DG
Finansinspektionen
IOSCO Member of the Board

Swedish DG of regulation and director of IOSCO.

341 John Abularrage
Head of US
TP ICAP

With Nick Deflora announced as stepping down from his role as CEO of ICAP Americas and deputy CEO of TP ICAP Americas at the end of December this year, John Abularrage, will take full responsibility for the region and oversee global broking for both brands as of January 2018.

342 Michael Loretan
Head of Asset Management division
FINMA
IOSCO Member of the Board

Swiss regulator who occupies a seat on the IOSCO board.

343 Rashed A. Al-Baloushi
CEO
Abu Dhabi Securities Exchange
Vice Chairman SAFE
FEAS Member of the Board

Rashed A. Al-Baloushi is also vice chairman of SAFE and a member of the board of the Arab Federation of Exchanges while celebrating five years as CEO of ADX in 2017.

344 Tajinder Singh
Deputy Secretary General
IOSCO

The former head of International Relations at SEBI has been Deputy Director General of IOSCO since 2009.

345 Eric Forest
CEO
EnterNext

Engaging CEO of the Euronext SME exchange business Enternext.

346 Mike Aikins
CTO
Chi-X Australia

Mike Aikins remains one of the clearest, straight-talking thinkers in the market technology space, across all areas of the stack including security. A former ASX CTO and longstanding advisor across the world who has been a part of key industry developments dating all the way back to the initial installation of ISE and beyond.

347 Tony Mackay
Independent

Tony MacKay is beavering away behind the scenes in the parish on new ventures, having most recently been chairman of Chi-X Australia, introducing JC Flowers to the acquisition of the platform and other tech assets from Nomura.

348 David Rutter
CEO
R3

David Rutter sits at the epicentre of one of many industry ventures in the distributed ledger.

349 Thomas A. Wittman
EVP Global Head of Equities
NASDAQ

Steeped in the equity options business, Wittman manages a diverse portfolio of US names under the NASDAQ banner.

350 Nondas Cl. Metaxas
CEO
Cyprus Stock Exchange

The likeable Nondas Metaxas has left the FESE board in recent times due to term limits but is a popular and involved boss of the Cyprus SE.

351-375

351 Nick Collier
Global Head of Government Relations
Thomson Reuters

Perhaps one of the most influential thinkers in the lobbying and regulatory space, Nick Collier maintains a goldplated Rolodex and is one of those figures with remarkable influence in regulatory discussions behind closed doors.

352 Ed Ditmire
Head of Investor Relations
NASDAQ

A former leading analyst with Fox Pitt and Kelton, Ed has done well as the IR boss of NASDAQ and continues to maintain a high ranking amongst investors.

353 Ki Won Kang
President & CEO of Derivatives Market
KRX

Overseas a veritable niche derivatives powerhouse business.

354 Hamed Ali
CEO
NASDAQ Dubai

Hamed Ali has been CEO of NASDAQ Dubai since 2013 and has long been involved with the planning and organisation of the Dubai financial infrastructure.

355 Jerome Kemp
Global Head Futures Clearing & Collateral Management
Citigroup Global Markets
FIA Vice-Chairman

Vice chairman of FIA and a leading figure in the FCM community.

356 Martin Pluves
CEO
LCH

Runs the London Clearing House arm of the LSE Group CCP entity.

357 Maroun Edde
CEO
Murex

MUREX retains power from straddling the OTC-ETD marketplace having emerged from the historic cluster of French vendors which grew from the 1980s onwards.

358 Robin Martin
MD Market Infrastructure
World Gold Council

Not highly visible but the man behind the WGC's move towards an exchange operation following the July 10th 2017 launch of LMEPrecious.

359 Kesara Manchusree
President
The Stock Exchange of Thailand
WFE Member of the Board

Mrs Kesara Manchusree presides over SET with a strong interest in multiple entities and projects such as SME funding and entrepreneurship as well as sitting on the board of WFE.

360 David Puth
CEO
CLS

For as long as forex clears via CLS, their CEO will retain parish clout.

361 Ray Cahnman
Chairman
Transmarket Group

A veteran market maker and proprietary trader who is synonymous with bonds. Many might have forgotten that he has traded in Sydney as well as Chicago.

362 Ade Cordell
Global Head of Equity Derivatives
ICE

As Global Head of Equity Derivatives for ICE, the only way I can foresee Ade Cordell losing influence in the parish in the short term is if he ends up being headhunted as the next James Bond. With Daniel Craig apparently signed for another 2 films, this looks to be a distant concern for now.

363 Richard Olsen
Founder
Lykke

Formerly the founder of OANDA, now parlaying what is essentially a market making company for anything on the DL. One of the brightest thinkers and persistently ahead of the curve, Richard Olsen is in a fascinating position with his latest venture which is seeking various regulatory permissions including an MTF licence in the EU.

364 Daniel Yergin
Vice Chairman
IHS Markit

I stand to be corrected but I believe Daniel Yergin is the only Pulitzer prize winning author in this listing and his work is something all parishioners ought to read and consider. As vice chairman of Markit and now IHS Markit, (having originally had his Cambridge Economic Research Associates acquired by Markit), he is a key thinker who was advising President Trump after his election in 2016.

365 Andres Ponte
Chairman
ROFEX

Came through the Cargill school of commodity trading, with a long association with ROFEX, Argentina's dynamic commodity marketplace.

366 Lilian Del Carmen Rocca Carbajal
Chairman
Superintendencia del Mercado de Valores
IOSCO Member of the Board

Lilian Del Carmen Rocca Carbajal is chairman of the Peruvian Regulator and sits on the board of IOSCO.

367 Adrian Tobias
Financial Counsellor & Director of the Monetary and Capital Markets Department
IMF

A former SVP of the New York Fed, Adrian Tobias leads the IMF's work on financial sector surveillance, monetary and macroprudential policies, financial regulation, debt management, and capital markets.

368 Craig Pirrong
Professor Bauer College of Business
University of Houston

Craig Pirrong blogs as "the Streetwise Professor" and it is an apt epithet. Rarely far removed from discussions about US derivatives, especially in energy and commodities, he is relaxed, pithy and concise with his informative interventions on markets.

369 Rick Lane
CEO
Trading Technologies

CTO since 2012, CEO since 2014, taking over from founder/majority owner now chairman, Harris Brumfield, Lane oversees one of the most influential vendors particularly in the derivatives marketplace.

370 Jim Rogers
Chairman
Rogers Holdings

A high profile investor best known for his "Investment Biker" and related travelogues, Jim happens to have a close involvement in the parish, including stakes in MOEX and the fledgling Singapore Diamond Exchange SDiX.

371 Tina Hasenpusch
CEO
CME Clearing Europe

Dr Tina Hasenpusch may be closing down the CME Europe CCP of which she has been CEO for the past two years but it appears at the time of writing she is set to continue with CME in a global clearing role.

372 Chaiyawat Wibulswasdi
Chairman
The Stock Exchange of Thailand

Chaiyawat Wibulswasdi was the former Central Bank Governor and has advised the Finance Minister amongst others in Thailand. He has an MIT PhD dating back to 1973, which somewhat pre-dates even the allure of MIT digital PhDs.

373 Jeffrey Tessler
MD for Clients, Products & Core Markets
DB

Jeff Tessler announced he would not seek a renewal of his contract and as such has already plummeted on the parish list of influence. Retained in name only but clearly at a level much reduced; merely a factor of time decay on his contract. May of course appear in a new position but it is thought after many lucrative years at DB1, he may yet head into retirement. And no, nobody is sure about that fabled Luxembourg butler or what may become of him (if he truly existed).

374 Tom Caldwell
Chairman
CSE & Caldwell Securities

In some respects the original pure play investor when he bought NYSE seats en masse, Caldwell retains a series of stakes around the parish.

375 Ruth Crowell
CEO
LBMA

The London Bullion Market head is in the vanguard of trying to maintain the relevance of the LBMA in a much more competitive marketplace than has been the traditional gold fix environment where historically the LBMA flourished.

376-400

376 Vahdettin Ertas
Chairman
Capital Markets Board, Turkey
IOSCO Member of the Board

Vahdettin Ertas is the chairman of the Turkish Capital Markets Board and sits on the board of IOSCO.

377 Michael Syn
EVP Head of Derivatives
SGX

Cambridge PhD who cut his teeth (by his own admission) "fetching the tea" for O'Connor folks settled at UBS and ended up as a key player in the SGX management team.

378 Alexey Rybnikov
President
SPIMEX

Amongst other influential positions in Russia, Alexey Rybnikov was formerly CEO of the MICEX Stock Exchange and senior vice president of MICEX prior to heading up the SPIMEX energy derivatives exchange.

379 Diego Fernandez
CEO
ROFEX

Diego Fernandez is CEO of the Argentine derivatives market ROFEX based in the city of Rosario.

380 Itai Ben-Zeev
CEO
TASE

After a rocky spell, TASE may finally be gaining a balance with Itai Ben-Zeev, a former Bank Leumi EVP taking over the reins just as the board appeared to push back on the chairman's control. The "startup nation" still needs to do a lot more for capital markets and there remains a horrible background of forex and binary charlatanry to eliminate beyond the legitimate boundaries of the Tel Aviv SE itself.

381 Don Wilson
CEO
DRW Member of the Board & Co-Founder DAH

Still in dispute with the CFTC which could see Don Wilson disappear from the parish if the regulator's action succeeds, Wilson's influence stems not merely from his pure proprietary trading activities, but also his founder status with Digital Asset Holdings.

As we closed for press DRW acquired another HFT market making company, RGM, run by Richard Gorelick (also on this list).

382 Sandra O'Connor
Chief Regulatory Affairs Officer
JPMorgan Chase & Co Chairman GFMA

As if being the Chief Regulatory Affairs officer of JP Morgan isn't enough, Sandra O'Connor is in the midst of her two year term as chairman of GFMA.

383 Hirander Misra
CEO & Co-Founder
GMEX

Hirander Misra may divide opinion in places but you can't stop him doing deals at a frenetic pace in faraway places. This year alone, a Lebanese CCP and a possible 5% stake in the Metropolitan Stock Exchange were his deals in the two months before this listing went to press while launching Vietnam's derivatives market.

384 Ludwik Sobolewski
CEO
Bucharest Stock Exchange

While it has been often rumoured that the PiS government in Poland would soon appoint Ludwik to high office, Sobolewski remains in situ in Bucharest on a handsome stipend by CEE/SEE standards while the exchange remains a passenger/prisoner of the low levels of function applicable to the Romanian state. However, as we closed for press it was announced Ludwik was out of contract and it appeared there may be some Romanian shenanigans about his renewal.

385 Mark G. Bagan
CEO
MGEX

As CEO of MGEX since 2005, Mark Bagan worked his way up from being a floor clerk, beginning in 1987. The exchange has been reporting remarkable volumes in recent months across various contracts thanks in part to the wheat shortages.

386 Simon Turek
Senior Director Government Relations
CME
EACHCCP.eu Chairman

Not clear what lies ahead for Simon now that the CME Europe clearing house is being closed down by its parent but he has been an active and popular chairman of the EACH.

387 Laurence Walton
Director of Exchange Regulation & Compliance
ICE

Another of the key 'eminence grise' figures in the parish. Few can surpass Laurence's vast depth of knowledge which effortlessly recollects a multitude of derivatives regulatory issues.

388 Rafael Plata
Secretary General
EACHCCP.eu

Having been nurtured amongst the excellent FESE team, Rafael is thriving as the Secretary General of the EU CCP federation EACH which he has steered with his typical elan despite limited resources. Respected in Brussels and amongst his members alike.

389 Khaled Al Khaled
CEO
Kuwait Stock Exchange

Lifelong experience in the Kuwaiti capital markets which dates back to those years rebuilding after the Iraq invasion.

390 Frank Wagener
Chairman
Luxembourg Stock Exchange

From the Banque International de Luxembourg to the chairmanship of the Luxembourg Stock Exchange, Frank Wagener's career has revolved around the Grand Duchy although he was also educated in part at Harvard.

391 Ivana Gazic
CEO
Zagreb Stock Exchange

In some ways the epithet 'indefatigable' would be a sound one for Ivana who has, for years, appeared to be in a Sisyphean position. However, Zagreb SE has been invigorated under her stewardship and she has acquired the Ljubljana exchange as well as listing her own company in recent years. She is a prime mover in the SEELink scheme and has an SME initiative alongside the SEELink backer EBRD. Dynamic and determined not to be beaten, she deserves much praise for her work.

392 Allison Parent
Executive Director
GFMA

A former Head of Global Policy and Strategy at Barclays, London (and earlier with Barclays in DC), Parent previously served as Senior Policy Advisor and Counsel for Markets at the Bank of England. To be based in Washington DC, Parent was appointed in June 2017 to replace NYC based Executive Director David Strongin who had previously signalled his intention to retire.

393 Mohamed Farid Saleh
Chairman Egyptian Exchange (EGX)
*ASEA Executive Committee member; FEAS, Chairman

*Strictly speaking positions held by retiring Chairman Mohamed Omran but presumably they will transfer.

Mohsen Adel took over at the expiry of academic Mohamed Omran's term on August 6th, 2017 as acting Chairman of the Egyptian SE but he was superseded within a week by Mohamed Farid Saleh who received a 4 year term from the government.

Modernising the Egyptian Stock Exchange against what has often been a difficult political background has proven challenging. Mohamed Farid Saleh has already expressed his desire to market Egypt more to international investors amongst other priorities for his term.

394 Carlos Lopez Marques
Deputy Director International Affairs Division
BME
FESE Member of the Board

Carlos maintains his position on the FESE board alongside his international responsibilities for BME which makes him frequently the face of the Spanish exchange seen outside Madrid.

395 Mao Zhirong
CEO
CESC

As the head of mainland development at HKEX, Mao Zhirong is a key player in building the linkages now powering HKEX forward. He is CEO of CESC (the jv of HKEX, Shanghai SFE and Shenzhen SZSE).

396 Mohammed Ahmed Alsaqqaf
Chairman
Kuwait Stock Exchange

Appointed as Kuwait Stock Exchange chairman in March 2017, Mohammed Ahmed Alsaqqaf replaced Essam Abdul Mohsen al-Marzouq who was promoted to head the oil Ministry by the Emir of Kuwait.

397 Marios A. Pilavakis
Chairman
Cyprus Stock Exchange
FESE Member of the Board

Marios Pilavakis joined the FESE board almost seamlessly after the departure of his CEO Nondas Metaxas who had reached his term limits.

398 Lars-Ivar Sellberg
Executive Chairman
Scila

As executive chairman of Scila, Lars-Ivar is a key player in the market surveillance industry.

399 Takehide Takahashi
CEO & Chairman
JCCH

It may not be the world's best known CCP but Japan Commodity Clearing House (JCCH) has significant clout.

400 Paul Conn
President Global Capital Markets
Computershare

Paul Conn's experience dates back to technology at the LSE in 1979 but he first came to parish prominence after 1989 when he joined ASX who then embarked on a series of fascinating developments such as going electronic, demutualising et al. Has been with Computershare since 1998, nowadays based in New York.

401-425

401 Maureen Downs
President
Rosenthal Collins Group
FIA Secretary

President of major FCM Rosenthal Collins & Secretary of the FIA.

402 Hannes Takacs
Senior Manager Local Currency & Capital Markets Development
EBRD

Hannes was a key figure within the Vienna Borse and built the best network of contacts across the New Europe. Unsurprising then that he was the ideal person to add heft to the EBRD after a spell consulting independently. Has helped create the excellent SeeLink amongst other EBRD sponsored projects.

403 Jacek Kubas
Principal Local Capital Markets
EBRD

Has been hugely influential in developing the fragmented and disorganised CEE/SEE capital markets where a lot more work is required, particularly as government apathy runs broadly amok through the region.

404 Sylvie Matherat
Chief Regulatory Officer
Deutsche Bank AG
Vice Chairman GFMA

In addition to being a leading figure in Deutsche Bank's regulatory activities Sylvie Matherat is vice chairman of GFMA.

405 Kirstina Combe
Head of Regulatory Strategy & Government Affairs
London Metal Exchange
FESE Member of the Board

The head of LME regulatory strategy is also a board member of FESE.

406 Lisa Kidd Hunt
EVP
Charles Schwab
Chairman-Elect SIFMA

As well as being an EVP of Charles Schwab, Lisa Kidd Hunt is chairman-elect of SIFMA.

407 Khalifa Bin Ebrahim Al Khalifa
CEO
Bahrain Bourse

Has been with Bahrain Bourse since 2010.

408 Brad Levy
CEO
Markitserv

As CEO of IHS Markit's powerhouse derivatives processing subsidiary MarkitServ, Brad Levy may well be unfairly treated by the EI1000 algorithm in this rating.

409 Matt Trudeau
President
Tradewind Markets (IEX)

A co-founder of the "Flash Boys" IEX project, Matt is concentrating on perhaps the least talked about blockchain project which is also the lowest profile new gold trading platform of the moment, TradeWinds Markets.

410 Christine Lagarde
MD
IMF

Like all good French politicians, Christine Lagarde has sailed through broadly without any career impact since her negligence conviction in 2016. The homilies about growth and suchlike continue to flow from the IMF boss but it all sounds a bit hollow these days. A pity that she appears in office but broadly without power in the era of political pygmies, as she retains one of the sharpest minds in or around the parish.

411 Rob Creamer
FIA PTG Chairman
Geneva Trading

Rob Creamer heads up Geneva Trading and chairs the FIA Principal Trading Group.

412 Remco Lenterman
FIA EPTA Chairman
Citadel Securities

HFT/algo/market making stalwart Remco Lenterman is chairman of the European FIA PTG having recently begun working for Citadel.

413 Guy Simpkin
Head of Business Development
BATS Europe

Guy Simpkin has an exciting toy box of opportunity at BATS Europe now overflowing with potential courtesy of the CBOE parent in Chicago. A proven innovator dating back to the best early swap future project, the LIFEE LFB, Guy has a practical understanding of market building and works well with BATS Europe's boss Mark Hemsley.

414 Rodrigo Buenaventura
General Director of Markets
CNMV

Having gained huge prominence via his ESMA role, Rodrigo Buenaventura has recently returned home to Spain as DG of CNMV, a role where he helps elevate the nation's regulatory status as well as providing excellent international insight honed from his years rattling around the Paris-Brussels milieu and the EU 28 as it was then.

415 Meyer "Sandy" Frucher
Vice-Chairman
NASDAQ
WFE Member of the Board

"Sandy" Frucher remains one of the entertaining figures in the parish where too many are dull suits. Having long overseen PHLX he positioned himself as NASDAQ Vice Chairman under Bob Greifeld and has been lapping the world with remarkable alacrity helping sell NASDAQ technology for some years. It remains unclear whether he is closer or further from power now Adena Friedman has taken over the reins of NASDAQ but he retains the company's WFE board seat.

416 Bruce Butterill
Executive Director
ACSDA

Bruce Butterill heads the CSD Association of the Americas which is Headquartered in Peru but working out of Bogota, Colombia.

417 Akinwumi Adesina
President
African Development Bank

As 9th president of the African Development Bank (elected in 2015), Akinwumi Adesina oversees the African Exchanges Linkage Project which is an endeavour to do for African exchanges what SEELink is doing for Eastern European markets.

418 Eddy Wymeersch
European Advisor & NED
AFME

Nowadays a European advisor and Member of the Board for AFME, Eddy Wymeersch retains significant clout as the former CEO of CESR.

419 Nader Azar
CEO
Amman Stock Exchange
AFE Chairman

Nader Azar, the Amman Stock Exchange CEO also sits on the board of the Arab Federation of Exchanges.

420 Carlo Koelzer
CEO
360T Group

Nowadays profiting from the acquisition by DB1 of 360T which he cofounded, Carlo Koelzer is a member of 360T's Group Executive Board and Deutsche Boerse Group Management Committee member as well as being titled Global Head of FX of Deutsche Boerse Group.

421 Patrick M. Byrne
CEO & founder
Overstock

Patrick M. Byrne has brushed off a serious medical scare (he had a three month leave of absence during 2016) and alongside his e-commerce platform is seeking to power a revolution driven by Blockchain on Wall Street. Issued his own stock on the Blockchain on December 20th.

422 Jacques Aigrain
Independent
NED
LSEG

Nowadays, Serial NED Jacques Aigrain sits on the board of LSE Group and on the periphery of the parish, Warburg Pincus, while he has our sympathies being burdened with a directorship of that fabulous beacon of customer obliviousness masquerading as an airline, Lufthansa.

423 Mark Austen
CEO
ASIFMA & GFMA

Mark Austen, CEO of ASIFMA took over as CEO of GFMA from Kenneth E. Bentsen, Jr in early 2016.

424 Laura Morrison
SVP Global Head of BATS Exchange-Traded Products
CBOE

While stock listings have proven difficult for BATS, Laura Morrison has helped build an ETF powerhouse for the Kansas City exchange which ought to be delivering remarkable synergy into the CBOE parent as well as being a growing source of excitement and content for the European business.

425 Ahmad Al-Marhoon
CEO
Muscat Securities Market
FEAS Vice-Chairman

FEAS Vice Chairman Ahmad Al-Marhoon runs the Muscat Securities Market and is chairman of the CSD.

426-450

426 James E. Oliff
Former Deputy Chairman
CME Group

There was a remarkable intake of breath around the parish when Jim Oliff resigned from the CME Group board just weeks ahead of the AGM (he was already on the slate, heading for an easy re-election). With this departure, Jim resigned his position in CME Europe and CME Clearing Europe. Formerly Deputy Chairman of CME Group and chairman of the influential Electronic Transition Committee which in essence formulated the path to digital markets which has propelled CME forward to this day (not that it was a solo effort, clearly then Chairman Scott Gordon and CEO Jim McNulty are just two names who deserve recognition amongst many). The sad and sorry tale of the CME's relative withdrawal from the world in early 2017 may yet become a management school case study. It's too early to say where that ends but Jim Oliff retains considerable influence in the parish as it is clear he will soon be shaping the future of market structure from another exciting position.

427 Michael Rudiger
Chairman
Dekabank
Chairman Frankfurt SE

Michael Rudiger was unanimously elected Chairman of Frankfurt SE by his fellow board members on June 1st 2017.

428 T. S. Krishna Murthy
Chairman
CDSL

TS Krishna Murthy has had somewhat of a baptism of fire, entering office and heading almost immediately into the excitement of the CDSL IPO process.

429 P. S. Reddy
CEO
CDSL

The CDSL is riding the crest of the wave after its superbly successful IPO just weeks before the EI1000 closed for press.

430 Jo Van De Velde
Head of Product Management
Euroclear

Jo Van de Velde heads the Euroclear Product Management division and is a member of the Euroclear Extended Management Committee. As an executive director and member of the board of Global Collateral Limited, the joint venture company between DTCC and Euroclear, he has global heft in the CSD world.

431 William H. Heyman
Vice Chairman & Chief Investment Officer
The Travelers Companies
Chairman FINRA

William H. Heyman, vice chairman and chief investment officer of The Travelers Companies, Inc., was elected FINRA chairman effective July 18th, 2017. Heyman earlier served as a member of the FINRA Board from January 2004 through September 2016.

432 Liu Fuzhong
Director of International Department

Shenzhen SE (SZSE)
Co-Chairman CESC (jv HKEX, SFE and SZSE)

As director of the international department at Shenzhen SE (SZSE), Liu Fuzhong adds to his parish influence as co-chairman of CESC the jv between HKEX, SFE and SZSE.

433 Shi Xiaocheng
Hong Kong Chief Representative
SSE
Co-Chairman CESC (jv HKEX, SFE and SZSE)

As the Hong Kong Chief Representative of the Shanghai Stock Exchange, Shi Xiaocheng's parish influence is enhanced by his role as co-chairman of CESC the jv between HKEX, SFE and SZSE.

434 Huw Jones
Journalist
Reuters

In an era when fake news predominates and where too many brands have opted for self-immolation, Reuters maintains a high quality roster of coverage. Nowhere is this better exemplified than in the person of the best exchange journalist, Huw Jones, who, ironically, is charged with a regulatory beat nowadays. Nevertheless he has a holistic understanding of parish matters (he was once also exchange correspondent before a spell in Brussels) and Huw maintains a killer Rolodex which he uses expertly to get to the bottom of tricky stories.

435 Morgan Downey
CEO
Money.net

Morgan Downey may have developed the terminal which kills the terminal duopoly. Maybe Reuters can survive but he looks likely to yet force major moves by the big two as his Money.net terminals are available at a fraction of the price of the incumbents. Thirty years after Bloomberg nearly ate Reuters, is Money.net about to end the Bloomberg era?

436 Larry Tabb
CEO
Tabb Group

Larry Tabb is an archetypal consultant in the parish and his almost Svengali-like hold over many on Wall Street is a treat to behold. Great with cash market knowledge and the minutiae of Reg NMS and anything pertaining to decades of SEC shenanigans on Wall Street.

437 Ramon Monzon
CEO
Philippine SE

Ramon Monzon, 67, may be an accountant who entered the exchange CEO office via a non-exec board position (since 2015) with a fairly standard mantra promising to reduce brokers' ownership of the bourse, refine rules on short-selling and introduce structured warrants. His career colour comes from his position as chairman and president of Carousel Productions Inc. which owns and runs the Miss Earth beauty contest.

438 Kaidi Ruusalepp
CEO & founder
Funderbeam

The former NASDAQ Estonia boss Kaidi Ruusalepp has powered the Blockchain forward in the parish through her venture Funderbeam which has a fascinating opportunity to become a leading SME marketplace.

439 Richard Thornhill
Chairman
LME Clear

Slaughter & May veteran lawyer Richard Thornhill has chaired the LME's standalone CCP since its foundation in 2013.

440 Guillaume Prache
MD
Better Finance

Guillaume Prache champions the European small investor and retail finance user albeit one does feel EU small investors ought to be given some form of endangered species designation given how hard the EU makes it for them to actually do anything worthwhile to add to their savings and investments.

441 Ed Boyle
CEO
BOX Options Exchange

BOX may no longer be the poster child of revolution in single name US equity options it once was but it survives, managed by Ed Boyle.

442 Otto Naegeli
NED Chairman
CME Clearing Europe

Otto Naegeli may have lost his chairmanship of CME Europe CCP but he remains on the board of the Bucharest SE at the encouragement of the EBRD while being a well-known player behind the scenes across the industry.

443 Venkat Chary
Chairman
FT India (now 63moons)

Venkat Chary was elevated from the board to chairmanship of FTIL in 2014 with Jignesh Shah under arrest and a forcible divestment of MCX being pushed. He appears to have steadied the ship for now but the influence of FTIL overall is a fraction of where it was when Jignesh Shah appeared to have a form of MOU status. Having proactively approached the authorities, it ought to be noted that Chary is not being probed as part of the ongoing investigation into the NSEL fiasco.

444 Fadi Khalaf
Secretary General
Arab Federation of Exchanges

The former Beirut SE CEO Fadi Khalaf has been Secretary General of the Arab Federation of Exchanges since 2009.

445 Karim Hajji
CEO
Casablanca Stock Exchange
ASEA, Deputy President

The ASEA deputy president is planning to sell the Casablanca SE's stock in an IPO within the next five years, he told Reuters in late 2016.

446 Fabrice Demarigny
Head of Financial Advisory & Capital Markets
Mazars
NED European Wholesale Securities Market, ECMI etc

As Head of Financial Advisory & Capital Markets for Mazars, the former CESR Secretary General Fabrice Demarigny maintains close relations with his welter of EU contacts and chairs ECMI while being on the board of the European Wholesale Securities Market jv of the Irish SE and the Malta SE.

447 Guy America
Co-Head of Global Credit Securitised Products & Public Finance
J.P. Morgan
AFME Vice-Chairman

Guy America is also vice chairman of GFMA.

448 Jose Antonio Martinez
CEO
Bolsa de Comercio de Santiago
FIAB, President

The CEO of the Santiago exchange, José Antonio Martínez is also the president of FIAB.

449 Dr. Jawad Anani
Chairman
Amman Stock Exchange

Dr Jawad Anani became chairman of Amman SE just as we closed for press in late August 2017. He only joined the board a month earlier on July 26th as a government appointee to the new joint stock company of the ASE founded in February under government control.

450 Jose T. Pardo
Chairman
The Philippine Stock Exchange

Former Secretary of the Department of Finance (2000-2001) and Secretary of the Department of Trade and Industry (1998-2000), Jose T. Pardo retains a roster of non-executive positions in the Philippines as well as chairing the domestic exchange.

451-475

451 Philip Stafford
Editor FT Trading Room
FT

The amiable Philip Stafford retains influence as essentially the only fully devoted parish exchange/market structure correspondent in the legacy media. Now under Nikkei ownership, it is unclear how long the FT can survive on its tight rope of EU fanaticism at the expense of objective journalism but Phil has endeavoured to put aside his socialist leanings to give the parish clear coverage.

452 Wieslaw Rozlucki
Co-Founder & former Chairman & CEO
GPW

It is both a testament to his longstanding merits and also a damning indictment of the state of Poland's government-markets nexus that despite being out of office at GPW for some time, Wieslaw remains the most influential Polish exchange figure. Summarily removed from office by the knee jerk actions of a new government, GPW has fallen into a tailspin since Dr Rozlucki's departure.

453 Timothy C. Scheve
President & CEO
Janney Montgomery Scott
Chairman
SIFMA Chairman

Timothy C. Scheve is chairman of SIFMA.

454 Geoffrey Odundo
CEO
Nairobi Securities Exchange
ASEA member of Executive Committee

The investment banker turned Nairobi SE CEO Geoffrey Odundo has overseen Nairobi SE since shortly after its IPO as well as sitting on the Executive Committee of ASEA.

455 Sunil Benimadhu
CEO
The Stock Exchange of Mauritius
WFE Member of the Board

Formerly with the ADB, the Stock Exchange of Mauritius CEO Sunil Benimadhu also sits on the WFE board.

456 Zeona Jacobs
Director Marketing & Corporate Affairs
Johannesburg Stock Exchange (JSE)
ASEA member of Executive Committee

Zeona Jacobs is JSE director of Marketing and Corporate Affairs and a member of the Executive Committee of ASEA.

457 Slawomir Panasiuk
Vice President of the Management Board
KDPW

Slawomir Panasiuk has been with KDPW Poland's CSD and CCP for over a decade.

458 Fiona Le Poidevin
CEO
TISE

The change of name to The International Stock Exchange (a title the LSE tried for an ill-fated period of months 30 years ago) may place the Channel Islands Exchange at risk of sounding grandiose but they have opened an office in the Isle of Man. Fiona Le Poidevin has done a terrific job steadying the CISX after the mini scandals of the CISE era and maintaining a strong presence as a listing venue which is neatly exposing the suicidal stance of the EU via MIFID II and other laws which some might say look expressly created to destroy capital markets, not improve them.

459 Edoh Kossi Amenounve
CEO
Bourse Regionale des Valeures Mobilieres
ASEA member of Executive Committee

Edoh Kossi Amenounve is a member of the ASEA Executive Committee as well as CEO of BRVM, the exchange intending to provide a unified bourse structure across eight West African nations, namely Benin, Burkina Faso, Ivory Coast, Guinea Bissau, Mali, Niger, Senegal and Togo.

460 Roger Peleback
CEO
Nordic Growth Market

Roger Peleback is the CEO of the Nordic Growth Market subsidiary of Boerse Stuttgart.

461 Steve Janjic
CEO
Americanex

Steve Janjic has assembled a fascinating group of mostly former NYMEX folks to create Americanex, the hemp futures exchange which also appears to have a good market valuation as it seeks to work through the gradual legalisation process of marijuana related products.

462 Serge Harry
Chief of Staff to Group CEO
LSEG

The veteran exchange executive Serge Harry continues to advise Xavier Rolet as well as serving as LSE's point man for the Benelux, France and Germany as well as chairing the GlobeSettle venture.

463 Alex Matturri
CEO
S&P Dow Jones Indices

Formerly senior vice president and director of Global Equity Index Management at Northern Trust Global Investments, Alex Matturri has run the largest household name index franchise in the parish since 2012 and also chairs the Index Industry Association.

464 Alfred Eskandar
CEO
Portware

Alfred Eskandar remains in charge at Portware following the 2015 acquisition by Factset Research Systems.

465 Luc Vansteenkiste
Chairman
European Issuers

A former president of the Federation of Belgian Enterprises, Luc Vansteenkiste has enjoyed a rich career in Belgian industry and is an active chairman of the European Issuers organisation championing publicly listed companies.

466 Simon Puleston Jones
Head of Europe
FIA

Former banker Simon Puleston Jones is also chairman of the Joint Trade Association Group while running the FIA European office.

467 John Deters
Chief Strategy Officer
CBOE

In a parish where those with the term 'Strategy' in their title usually have little real strategic responsibility, John Deters has been behind fascinating minority stakes in Eris Exchange and Curve Global as well as playing his role in the transformative BATS deal.

468 Bruce Aust
Vice-Chairman
NASDAQ

Bruce Aust represents NASDAQ out west where it has an Entrepreneurial centre while playing a pivotal role in his current and previous positions (as EVP Global Listings Services) in securing a panoply of top tier IPOs to NASDAQ.

469 Haroon Askari
Acting CEO

Pakistan Stock Exchange (PSX)
Member of the Board SAFE

The Pakistan exchanges have been resolved into one mega stock market with Chinese cornerstone shareholders and the exchange has been listed – quite a year or two!

CEO Nadeem Naqvi left office after the IPO had been completed and and his term expired. Haroon Askari has been running the company since but local media stories as we closed for press suggested Canadian Richard Wilson was being lined up for the job.

470 Christopher T. Matzdorf
Chairman
MGEX

Commodity veteran and longstanding MGEX board member Christopher T. Matzdorf has chaired MGEX since 2015.

471 Richard Schaeffer
Chairman
Americanex

Former NYMEX chairman Richard Schaeffer provided some additional heft when he joined the Americanex board in 2015.

472 Karel Lannoo
CEO
CEPS
Director ECMI

Karel Lannoo has been CEO and responsible for finance at the CEPS think tank since 2000. Also a director of the ECMI.

473 Magnus Haglind
Head of Global Commodities
NASDAQ

Magnus Haglind is COO of NASDAQ Global Commodities, based in Stockholm but with an interest in ventures such as the US based NFX.

474 Marcos Ayerra
Chairman
Comision Nacional de Valores, Argentina
IOSCO Member of the Board

The chairman of the Argentine regulator is also on the board of IOSCO.

475 Bob Caisley
SVP Technology Systems
NASDAQ

Bob Caisley has vast parish IT experience with ASX and SGX, while he is now senior vice president of Technology System in Stockholm where Peter Jessup was previously stationed in the same role before he returned to Sydney.

476-500

476 Aliko Dangote
President
Nigerian SE

Akin Dangote is the richest man in Nigeria. His interests range far and wide across both sectors and enterprises. This hugely adds to his influence quotient given his position as chairman of the Nigerian Stock Exchange which is currently awaiting parliamentary approval to list its own shares (the bill was progressing as the EI1000 went to press).

477 Eric Scott Hunsader
CEO & Founder
Nanex

Eric Scott Hunsader is nowadays less famous for his own excellence in algorithmic systems design as for his excellence in calling out the excesses of HFT which he has rigorously analysed for many years.

478 Martin Fraenkel
President
S&P Global Platts

Martin Fraenkel is president of S&P Global Platts, which he joined in June 2015 having previously been Global Head of Energy at CME. He is a member of the Council of Chatham House, The Royal Institute of International Affairs.

479 Patrick L Young
Exec Director
DV Advisors
Founder / Publisher Exchange Invest & EI1000

Obscurely noted online for his remark "The trouble with weather forecasting is that it's right too often for us to ignore it and wrong too often for us to rely on it." Perhaps Patrick L Young has found himself in a situation where "The trouble with a 1000 person influencers list is many are too high on the list to ignore or too low to be taken seriously." With regular contact to the world's biggest markets he is clearly directly part of the influencers' stream throughout the parish.

480 Yousuf Abdulla Humood
Chairman
Bahrain Bourse

The Bahrain Bourse chairman, Yousuf Abdulla Humood, is also deputy chairman of the Arab Investment Company.

481 Dr Okwu Joseph Nnanna
Chairman
FMDQ OTC Securities Exchange

Chairing the licensed OTC market in Nigeria, Dr Nnanna is the Deputy Governor, Financial System Stability, Central Bank of Nigeria (CBN). He also currently oversees the CBN's Economic Policy Directorate, which comprises the Financial Markets Department, amongst others. He represents the CBN on the Board of FMDQ. He is the Chair of the Africa Finance Corporation and a life member of the Nigerian Economic Society. He has served on the Boards of many organisations, including the Board of the International Monetary Fund.

482 Mauro Dognini
GM
Monte Titoli
ECSDA Executive Committee member

Mauro Dognini was appointed GM of the Italian CSD within LSEG, Monte Titoli in 2014.

483 Mohamed Omran
Chairman
Egyptian Financial Supervisory Authority
Member of the IOSCO Board

Mohamed Omran's term as Egyptian Exchange Chairman expired on August 6th 2017 and he was temporarily replaced by Mohsen Adel with Mohamed Farid Saleh confirmed for a 4 years term less than a week later just as the EI1000 closed for press. However before Professor Omran could make a total return to academia, he was appointed acting Chairman of the Egyptian regulatory board, taking over from outgoing chairman Sherif S. Samy.

484 Eddie Astanin
CEO
NSD
ECSDA Executive Committee member

Eddie Astanin's NSD in Russia has been actually delivering bits of Blockchain tech here and there into its offering while others are talking. He is also an Executive Committee member of ECSDA.

485 Dawn DeBerry Stump
Commissioner (nominee)
CFTC

Former NYSE Euronext staffer Dawn DeBerry Stump has been nominated as a CFTC commissioner. She is currently president of Stump Strategic, a consulting firm, while she previously worked in the Senate Committee on Agriculture, Nutrition and Forestry, focussing on farm policy matters and the CFTC.

486 Marek Dietl
CEO
Warsaw SE

Marek Dietl is the latest CEO of Warsaw Stock Exchange (WSE). An economist, he recently has served as a member of the board of the WSE. Polish Radio cited Dietl saying, "One of the ways to build scale is a strategic alliance. I believe that in certain market niches in Central and Eastern Europe there is an opportunity to build strategic alliances." So in other words, he got the job on the basis of politics.

487 Werner Frey
Director of Post Trade
AFME
Former CEO of ESF (European Securities Forum)

Werner Frey is the former CEO of ESF (European Securities Forum) and nowadays the director of Post Trade for AFME.

488 Gyorgy Dudas
CEO
KELER
ECSDA Vice-Chairman

Gyorgy Dudas is a veteran of CEE markets from his position running Keler; he is also deputy chairman of the ECSDA and has long been involved with AFM and other organisations.

489 Kevin Heffron
COO
Trayport

As Trayort COO, Kevin Heffron brings over 40 years of commodity trading experience to the table. It will be interesting to see the direction of travel for Trayport now that the ICE appear destined to sell off their acquisition due to the UK CMA's concerns.

490 Amir Hamooni
CEO
Iran Fara Bourse

Amir Hamooni has been CEO of Iran Fara Bourse and a member of the Iran Financial Centre board for 5 years.

491 David G. Downey
CEO
OneChicago

David G. Downey has been CEO of OneChicago for 10 years, having previously been closely involved on several market floors and working amongst other places for Timber Hill.

492 Antonio L. Delise
CFO
MarketAxess

Antonio L. Delise has been CFO since 2010.

493 Florence Bindelle
SG
European Issuers

Florence Bindelle moved from running the the Federation of European Risk Management Associations (FERMA) to running the European Issuers organisation with gusto in the eye of the excitement of CMU which might yet prove a useful turning point for European investment.

494 Richard Vegh
Chairman & CEO
Budapest Stock Exchange

Richard Vegh was elevated to run the Budapest SE when the Central Bank acquired if from the CEESEE Group.

495 Mounir Gwarzo
Director General
SEC Nigeria
IOSCO Member of the Board

Mounir Gwarzo is a member of the board of IOSCO and DG of the Nigerian regulator.

496 Ivan Takev
CEO
Bulgarian Stock Exchange

Ivan Takev has been CEO of the Bulgarian SE since 2008 and was amongst the co-founders of the SEELink project. He is a staunch champion of his national market with an enthusiastic resolve to improve the local and regional capital markets.

497 Adam Eades
Chief Legal & Regulatory Officer
BATS Europe

As Chief Legal and Regulatory Officer of BATS Europe, Adam Eades has been with the firm for six years having previously worked alongside BATS Europe CEO Mark Hemsley at LIFFE where Adam spent 14 years. One of those useful figures who can influence regulatory debate and thus has influence behind closed doors.

498 Ahmad Sharaf
Chairman
Dubai Mercantile Exchange

Ahmad Sharaf chairs DME having also previously worked as head of strategy for Dubai Holdings. Nowadays he is CEO of Dutco Energy, part of the Dutco Group.

499 Andrew Ng
Group Executive Head of Treasury & Markets
DBS Bank
Chairman ASIFMA

Andrew Ng is chairman of ASIFMA and the head of Treasury Markets for the Singaporean city state's homegrown powerhouse DBS Bank.

500 Mary Schapiro
Independent NED

As someone approaching a legendary figure in regulation, Mary Schapiro has chaired CFTC and SEC as well as coordinating the deal that created FINRA from NASD and NYSE Regulation.

501-526

501 Marlene Street Forrest
CEO
Jamaica Stock Exchange

Marlene Street Forrest's lengthy tenure of Jamaica SE has included a very successful IPO of the market itself while in October 2016 she was awarded the Jamaican Order of Distinction in the Rank of Commander.

502 Charles P. Carey
NED
CME Group

The CBOT chairman who oversaw the takeover by CME, Charles P. Carey retains influence within CME and across Chicago.

503 Nandini Sukumar
CEO
WFE

Plucked from the Bloomberg journalistic team where she had a reputation for diligence and sound reporting, Nandini was brought in to run the WFE at the behest of Andreas Preuss via a lower office before succeeding Huseyin Erkan. Saddled with a fractious organisation which lacks a general purpose, it is only fair to say that Nandini is struggling and is indeed finding it hard to engage the broader exchange community beyond the relatively narrow scope of the WFE membership, which really does not reflect the modern world of exchanges.

504 Jorge Hernan Jaramillo
President
Deceval
ACSDA President, WCSDA President

The Deceval (Colombian CSD) President Jorge Hernán Jaramillo is currently also president of the ACSDA and the WCSDA.

505 John F. (Jack) Sandner
NED
CME & Dubai Mercantile Exchange

Jack Sandner retains his board seat at CME (he is a past chairman, having joined the board in 1978) and also sits on the board of DME in Dubai (representing CME) as well as the Virtu board and the NFA board.

506 James Overdahl
Partner
Delta Strategy Group
FIA Member of the Board

James Overdahl was once chief economist of SEC and has been with Delta Strategy Group since 2013 as a partner alongside founding partner Jim Newsome. Overdahl also sits on the FIA board.

507 Dimitris Karaiskakis
COO
Helex

Dimitris Karaiskakis has worked his way up the Athex chain of command to COO having started with the IT subsidiary in 1997.

508 Rijnhard Van Tets
Chairman
Euronext

Rijnhard van Tets chairs the Euronext Supervisory Board and chairs the Nomination and Governance Committee. He was appointed to the Supervisory Board of Euronext N.V. in 2003 and became chairman in 2007. He is also the chairman of the Board of Euronext Amsterdam N.V. He served as a director of NYSE Euronext from 2007 to 2013.

509 Pieter Schuurs
President & COO
ICE
Endex Europex Chairman, Europex General Assembly

Pieter Schuurs is president and COO of ICE Endex (of which ICE bought 100% control just as we closed for press with the EI1000). Schuurs is also chairman of the Europex General Assembly.

510 Gerard Scully
Director of International Primary Markets
Irish Stock Exchange

Gerard Scully has been director of International Primary Markets of The Irish Stock Exchange since February 2008. Gerard chairs the Irish chapter of ICMA as well as being a member of the ESMA Corporate Finance Consultative Working Group.

511 Francis J. Troise
CEO & President
ITG

Francis J. Troise was parachuted in to ITG after an investor rebellion post SEC problems. While he spent eight years with ITG earlier in his career, he rejoined ITG after being head of J.P. Morgan Execution Services.

512 Dr Miroslav Budimir
SVP
Eurex

Dr Miroslav Budimir is an SVP at EUREX who maintains a regular stream of thinking, output, research and regulatory engagement.

513 Mark Beddis
Strategic Advisor
BIDS

Mark Beddis is somebody you really ought to know. Not a high profile figure in the BIDS enterprise (he lives in Vancouver) nonetheless the company has been shaped by his input. His considerable experience derives from the likes of Alberta Market Solutions which powered many a fledgling electronic market. Before that, during his time at the Hong Kong Futures Exchange, he was as a pioneer in their single stock futures products. Come to think of it, if you have clout, you probably already do know Mark.

514 Chip Dempsey
SVP & CCO
OCC

The SVP & CCO of OCC, Chip Dempsey, has responsibility for strategy, planning and business and product development efforts. He is active on the conference circuit.

515 David Newns
CEO
SwapEx

David Newns is a senior managing director at State Street and global head of Currenex as well as the chief executive officer for SwapEx. Back in 2001, he was a founding member of the London team at Currenex.

516 Claudio Zuchovicki
Secretary General
FIAB

Claudio Zuchovicki spent many years as commercial director of the Buenos Aires Bourse and has been director general of the FIAB (The South American Bourse Federation) since late in 2016.

517 Roberto Belchior
Director of LATAM Market Development
B3

Charged with market development in LatAM, Roberto Belchior occupies B3 board seats linked to the Brazilian exchange's stakes in Chile, Colombia and Peru.

518 James Miller
Chairman
NZX

James Miller chairs NZX and has been on the board since 2010. He maintains a portfolio of New Zealand board positions.

519 Mark Gorton
Founder & MD
Tower Research

Outside of Tower and its speedy trading, Mark Gorton has a portfolio of interests and is eager to reduce mankind's reliance on gas guzzling automobiles.

520 Paul Bowes
Director Benchmarks
Thomson Reuters

One of the most popular figures on this list, Canadian Paul Bowes is also amongst the best networkers in the parish. A Reuters veteran, he has worked in various other enterprises and is now overseeing the Reuters Index business.

521 David Wright
Chairman
Eurofi

David Wright remains renowned as one of the best thinkers ever to grace the EC's financial regulation arms then he headed IOSCO with gusto prior to heading over to Chair the Eurofi think tank in 2016 where he was probably the only person big enough to fill the shoes of the departing Chairman Jacques de Larosière.

522 Peter Gomber
Professor
University of Frankfurt

Peter Gomber is the leading German academic in the parish.

523 Antonella Amadei
Head of Global Development Market Infrastructures
LSEG

There are few single name brands in the industry – 'Antonella' is one of them. From Borsa Italiana to LSEG itself, she has worked with Millennium IT and now maintains a global roving brief in market structure for LSEG.

524 David Blitzer
MD & Chairman of the Index Committee
S&P Dow Jones Indexes

David Blitzer is MD and chairman of the Index Committee for S&P as well as a well-known author of financial tomes.

525 Michael Gooch
Executive Chairman
GFI Group

Having profited from the sale of GFI to BGC, "Mickey Gooch" may have surprised many by staying put within Howard Lutnick's empire. Meanwhile, his son Mickey Gooch Jnr has garnered fame and fortune as a movie actor.

526-550

526 Martin J. Gepsman
NED
CME Group

CME insider Marty Gepsman has sat on the CME board since 1994 and was secretary of the board from 1998 to 2007.

527 Howard J. Siegel
NED
CME Group

CME board member Howard J. Siegel is also the secretary and treasurer of the CME Group Foundation.

528 Mehtap Dinc
Member of the Executive Board
Eurex

Mehtap Dinc has worked her way up from product manager joining EUREX in 1999 to a seat on the executive board of EUREX Frankfurt, fulfilling a number of roles including in product development along the way.

529 Maurice Van Tilburg
CEO Euronext Amsterdam
Euronext

Qualified engineer Maurice Van Tilburg runs Euronext Amsterdam having begun his parish career with EOE in 1995 and then spending time with Euroclear.

530 Vincent Van Dessel
CEO Euronext Brussels
Euronext

Vincent Van Dessel began his career as a stockbroker before joining the Brussels Exchange in 1992 and working his way up to head the business in 2009.

531 Susan Estes
CEO
OpenDoor Trading

Bond market veteran Susan Estes is CEO of OpenDoor, a well-funded new bond market platform.

532 Mobis Phillipose
Journalist
Livemint

Mobis Phillipose retains a vast wealth of knowledge in Indian capital markets and thirsts to better understand the parish. By turns witty, pithy and insightful, he is a leader amongst a media pack covering the parish which is probably the most competitive in the world.

533 Angela Knight
Senior Independent NED
Tullet Prebon

Dame Angela Knight, one time Conservative minister apparently once nearly ran the WFE (back in the day when the WFE had money and indeed still thought it had a purpose) but plumped for a job running Energy UK instead. Perhaps most famous for running APCIMS and the British Bankers Association. Nowadays she retains a portfolio of directorships including with TP ICAP.

534 R. Cromwell Coulson
President & CEO
OTC Markets Group

Cromwell Coulson sees his OTC Markets Group as the "missing link" in capital markets for companies "left behind" when NASDAQ was upgraded to exchange status in 2006.

535 Ahmed Farhad
Enforcement & Cooperation Advisor
IOSCO

Ahmed Farhad had some 17 years of regulatory experience with the Bangladeshi SEC before joining IOSCO in 2015 as Enforcement and Cooperation Advisor.

536 Mark Peterson
CEO
NZX Limited

NZX CEO Mark Peterson was confirmed as CEO early in 2017 having been elevated from the acting role on the retirement of Tim Bennett.

537 Andrew Hauser
Director for Banking, Payments & Financial Resilience
Bank of England

"Much more work is needed across a whole range of issues, including: speed and confidentiality protections; developing common protocols; integrating cash and securities movements; and establishing regulatory and legal norms", remarked the Bank of England's resident thinker, Andrew Hauser, on the topic of Blockchain. Clearly not a standard run of the mill QE loon then.

538 Ketan Patel
Group Risk Officer
HKEx
Vice Chair of CCP12

Ketan Patel of HKEX occupies the company's CCP12 board position while overseeing risk by day.

539 Jenny Knott
CEO
NEX Optimisation

At the helm of a fascinating, er, 'NEX-us' of fintech possibility that may yet deliver a brave new world of post OTC processing, Jenny Knott has a high profile and a lot of projects which need to be executed and communicated well. It's a high stress position requiring not merely management but also a lot of digital nous.

540 Jean-Francois Conil-Lacoste
Exec Dir
Power Spot Markets
EEX Member of the Board, Europex

Europex Board Member, and leading figure in EPEX spot, Jean-Francois Conil-Lacoste is a parish veteran.

541 David Gurle
CEO & Founder
Symphony

David Gurle is the main man behind one of the more fascinating messaging initiatives which threatens to eat Bloomberg's lunch after Bloomie memorably dropped the ball by managing to leak data to its own journalists.

542 Christine Bortenlaenger
CEO
Deutsches AktienInstitut

Christine Bortenlaenger oversees the powerful German shareholder organisation.

543 Fred Hatfield
Senior Advisor
Patomak
NED NYSE

Fred Hatfield is a leading member of the Patomak team and sits on the board of NYSE having previously been a CFTC commissioner.

544 Leanne Parsons
Director Trading & Market Services
JSE

Leanne Parsons has been with JSE since 1985.

545 Hans-Peter Friedrich
Chairman German Coalition Government Brexit Group
Bundestag

Hans-Peter Friedrich chairs the German government's Brexit Group and, as such, is one of those people who will doubtless hear a lot from his own industrialists on both export and financing fronts, if the EU or the German government opts for a mutually assured destruction approach to Brexit.

546 Ashima Goyal
Chairman
MSEI

A professor at the Indira Gandhi Institute of Development Research, Mrs Ashima Goyal chairs the MSEI in the parish.

547 David Howson
COO
BATS Europe

David Howson was formerly CTO of Equiduct prior to becoming COO of BATS Europe.

548 Pawel Ostrowski
CEO
TGE/PolPX
Europex General Assembly

Paweł Ostrowski was appointed CEO of PolPX as part of the government's pogrom-esque management upheaval across much of the Polish government-controlled sector of industry and, er, enterprise. PolPX remains a formidable engine of profit at the GPW overall.

549 Ruhail Muhammad
Chairman
PMEX

Ruhail Mohammed is the nominee director of Securities & Exchange Commission of Pakistan (SECP) at PMEX. He is currently the chief executive officer of Engro Fertilizers Limited.

550 Jonathan Clark
CEO
Luminex

Jonathan Clark runs Luminex, a recent buyside initiative seeking to take on the block trading market.

551-575

551 Ejaz Ali Shah
MD
PMEX

Ejaz Ali Shah is managing director of Pakistan Mercantile Exchange having previously, served for 16 years as General Manager, Head of Marketing & Customer Support Services at Central Depository Company of Pakistan Limited (CDCPL).

552 Niki Beattie
CEO
Market Structure Partners
Chairman Aquis Exchange, Director Borsa Istanbul

Niki Beattie left the MOEX board and took up a position with BIST to add to her chairmanship of MTF Aquis and a wide roster of consulting the world over.

553 Stuart Connolly
CEO
TriOptima

Stuart Connolly replaced founder CEO Per Sjoberg at the helm of TriOptima earlier in 2017 with a remit to drive the historically mega-successful compression service forward.

554 Andre Roelants
Board of Directors
Clearstream Banking

Former Clearstream CEO Andre Roelants retains a position as honorary chairman.

555 Zhanat Kurmanov
Chairman
Kazakhstan Stock Exchange

The director of Insurance, the surveillance department of the National Bank of Republic of Kazakhstan since early 2016, Zhanat Kurmanov has been chairman of the board of the Kazakhstan Stock Exchange since 2012.

556 Darryll Hendricks
Americas Regional Operating Officer
UBS Investment Bank
Member of the Board DTCC

Regional operating officer in the Americas for UBS Investment Bank, Darryll Hendricks was formerly with the Federal Reserve. He also sits on the DTCC board.

557 Alina Aldambergen
CEO
Kazakhstan Stock Exchange
FEAS Working Committee Chairman

As CEO of KASE since early 2016, Alina Aldambergen has already refreshed the brand identity and introduced a new commercial bond segment with a significant plan for other developments. She also chairs the FEAS working committee.

558 Gary H. Stern
Member of the Board
DTCC

In 2004 Gary H Stern co-authored with Ron J. Feldman 'Too Big to Fail – The Hazards of Bank Bailouts' during his tenure as CEO of the Federal Reserve Bank of Minneapolis (1985-2009). He currently sits on the board of DTCC, E*TRADE Financial Corporation, S&P Global Ratings Ambac Assurance Corporation, the Council for Economic Education (CEE) amongst other entities.

559 James Davies
COO
London DX

James Davies cofounded GMEX and stayed with the spinout of London Derivatives Exchange which has developed a fascinating approach to the thorny issue of creating swap futures.

560 Jim Lee
COO
BIDS Trading

A founder and COO of BIDS Trading, Jim Lee was educated in western Canada, whence came many of the BIDS founders, in one way or another.

561 Justin Meadows
CEO
EBS Treasury

Justin Meadows is the CEO of NEX Treasury, the cash and FX liquidity management centre for corporates and banks who need the right amount of cash, in the right currency, in the right place – at the right time. Formerly known as MyTreasury, the project was initially funded by the European Commission to help enterprises.

562 Philip Allison
CEO
KCG Europe

Philip Allison, is CEO of KCG Europe Limited, having joined KCG in 2014 after a 17-year career at UBS, most recently as Global Head of Cash Equities and EMEA Head of Equities.

563 Roberto Gonzalez Barrera
CEO Post Trade
BMV
ACSDA Vice President

The post trade director of the Mexican exchange, Roberto Gonzalez Barrera is also vice president of the ACSDA.

564 Mark Carney
Governor
Bank of England
Chairman FSB

As governor of the Bank of England, Mark Carney is a serious AAA blobster aided by his previous Canadian government appointments and his years at Goldman Sachs. He joined the Bank on July 1st, 2013 and nowadays also serves as chairman of the Financial Stability Board (FSB), First Vice-Chair of the European Systemic Risk Board, a member of the Group of Thirty and the Foundation Board of the World Economic Forum. While he has influence, this doesn't always appear to convert into prescience. His wails of inaccurate balderdash about economic disaster proved to be as unwelcome as it was inaccurate during the UK EU referendum of 2016.

565= Stuart Lucas
Founder & Co-CEO
AssetMatch

Head of Credit Trading at Nomura until 2009 after a plethora of similar roles, Stuart Lucas has over 35 years of fixed income experience.

565= Iain Baillie
Founder & Co-CEO
AssetMatch

With, like his co-founder Stuart Lucas, some 35 years' experience in debt markets, prior to co-founding Asset Match, Iain Bailie was, amongst other roles, CEO of MarketAxess Europe from 2003 to 2007.

566 Zafar Abdullah
Chairman
SEC Pakistan
IOSCO Member of the Board

SEC commissioner Zafar Abdullah has been promoted to the top spot of the Pakistan SEC at least in the interim following the fall from grace of chairman Muhammad Zafar-Ul-Haq Hijazi during July 2017 when he was arrested for tampering with official records. Nevertheless the SECP has some issues as the most senior commissioner ought to be appointed to the job of chairman. However, the most senior commissioner Tahir Mahmood is apparently also bound up in the same investigation...

567 Cristobal Conde
Executive In Residence
Yale U FinTech Innovation Lab
Chairman Calastone, Board Member DAH, OpenGamma etc

Ran Sungard for nine years and in retirement is in and around the fintech space with a few executive in residence positions as well as sitting on the board of Digital Asset Holdings amongst others.

568 Jeffrey Hogan
Senior MD, Global Head, Client & Regulatory Liaison
BGC Partners

Spending a rather spectacular 26 years with BGC is a remarkable achievement. Jeff Hogan remains engaged across the parish and fixed income in particular as senior managing director, Global Head of Client & Regulatory Liaison.

569 Sergei Mayorov
Group Strategy Director
MOEX

As director of Group Strategy, Sergei Mayorov has long had a sound understanding of what makes markets tick and how to build the Russian marketplace.

570 Sunil Hirani
Co-Founder & CEO
trueEX
Member of the Board, co-founder DAH

Sunil Hirani sold Creditex to ICE in 2008 and is nowadays building Truex (not to be confused with the earlier TruExchange of circa 2000 AD) while recently he garnered a lot of headlines for suing IHS Markit over access to data at MarkitServ.

571 Erica Brown
Head of International Affairs, NASDAQ Clearing
NASDAQ
Board Member of CCP12 and EACH

Erica Brown is head of international affairs for the excellent NASDAQ Scandinavian CCP while also serving on the boards of both EACH and CCP-12.

572 Vijay Kishanlal Kedia
CEO & President
FlexTrade

The FlexTrade CEO, Vijay Kishanlal Kedia has built the company over the span of more than 20 years.

573 Andy Ross
CEO
CurveGlobal

Andy Ross was garlanded with media commentary on his appointment in early 2016 making comparisons with difficult football management. This is odd as, in the main, I think even those who aren't interested in soccer can see the point in football teams. Presumably it's a poisoned chalice comparison as overall there is a veritable paucity of plausible reasons to create the Curve platform other than perhaps reducing the LSEG corporate taxation bill. That said, having been CEO of one platform and having kept the lights on for a year already without blotting his own copybook, Andy has been doing a decent job.

574 Chris Sturgess
Director Commodity Derivatives
JSE
AFM Chairman

The JSE director of Commodity Derivatives (de facto head of what was SAFEX), Chris Sturgess is the first multi-term AFM chairman, having been in office since 2013.

575 Ralph Danielski
Director
Boerse Stuttgart

Ralph Danielski is a member of the executive Board of Boerse Stuttgart GmbH (since 2015), speaker of the executive board of EUWAX AG, and a director of the Boerse Stuttgart subsidiary Nordic Growth Market.

576-600

576 Anna Kulik
Secretary General
ECSDA

Anna Kulik moved from Euroclear to replace Soraya Belghazi as secretary general of ECSDA in May 2017.

577 Kay Swinburne
MEP
Chairman of NEX Reg think tank

"I, along with MEPs from other parts of the EU, have previously criticised the way in which the EU has an equivalence process that is highly politicised." Just one of many pithy missives from the soon not to be an MEP Kay Swinbourne, when Brexit goes through in March 2019.

578 Murat Cetinkaya
CEO & Deputy Chairman
Borsa Istanbul

Halk Investment CEO Murat Cetinkaya was elected as the new CEO of Turkey's main stock exchange Borsa Istanbul, replacing Osman Sarac, during the bourse's 4th Ordinary General Board Meeting on June 8th, 2017 as well as deputy chairman of BIST amongst other group appointments.

579 Tim Ward
CEO
Quoted Companies Alliance

Tim Ward runs the UK small to mid-sized Quoted Companies Alliance. His past roles have included Head of Issuer Services at the London Stock Exchange.

580 Juan Andres Camus
Chairman
Bolsa Comercio Santiago

Juan Andrés Camus chairs the Santiago exchange having been on the board since 2010 while also chairing BTG Pactual in Chile.

581 Anna Ewing
CEO
Anna's Angels
NED NEX Group

Longstanding NASDAQ staffer Anna Ewing has various activities in the VC field these days while in the parish, she was appointed to the board of NEX earlier in 2017.

582 Mohammadreza Mohseni
President & CEO
CSDIran
FEAS member of exec board

Mohammadreza Mohseni is president and CEO of CSD Iran and sits on the board of FEAS.

583 Yoshiaki Koike
Chairman
Sapporo Stock Exchange

Yoshiaki Koike heads the Sapporo Exchange which is little known outside Japan but has some regional clout, and even had an IPO as recently as June 2017 (Ecomott).

584 Ulf Noren
Global Head of Sub-Custody
SEB

Ulf is perhaps the most omnipresent man in custody pertaining to Europe with a remarkable client footprint and a simply unparalleled Rolodex and name recognition in the field.

585 Tito Sulistio
President Director
Indonesia Stock Exchange

Tito Sulistio is president director of the Indonesian Stock Exchange until 2018. Away from his extensive industrial career, he is a passionate collector of classic motorcycles.

586 Hasan Ghalibaf Asl
CEO
Tehran Stock Exchange
FEAS, member of exec board

Hasan Ghalibaf Asl runs the Tehran SE and is a member of the board of FEAS.

587 B. Nyamaa
Chairman
Mongolian Stock Exchange

Mr B. Nyamaa serves as Head of Financial Policy, Debt Management Department, Ministry of Finance, and has been chairman of the Mongolian Stock Exchange since June 2014.

588 Andre Kuusvek
Director
EBRD
FEAS, Member of exec board

Andre Kuusvek serves not only as a director of local currency and capital market initiatives in the EBRD but also on the board of FEAS.

589 Richard Ketchum
Member of the board
MarketAxess

Former FINRA CEO Richard Ketchum is a NED at MarketAxxess.

590 Jonathan Herbst
Global head of financial services
Norton Rose Fulbright

A longstanding and diligent lawyer at Norton Rose, Jonathan Herbst has rightfully risen to become Global head of financial services at the enlarged firm.

591 Howard Edelstein
Chairman
Redi Holdings
Member of the Board Algomi

Redi Holdings Chairman Howard Edelstein is also on the board of Algomi.

592 Michael Krogmann
Member of the management board
Frankfurt SE (DB1)

Michael Krogmann is a member of the Frankfurt Stock Exchange management board within DB1.

593 Abdul Wahed Al Fahim
Chairman
NASDAQ Dubai

Abdul Wahed Al Fahim is a member of the Board of Directors of Dubal Holding, Emirates Global Aluminium, Emirates Development Bank, Meydan City Corporation and Union National Bank and chairman of NASDAQ Dubai.

594 Sir Brian Bender
Chairman
LME

Sir Brian Bender was appointed chairman of the LME in 2010 having retired from the UK civil service in 2009 after almost a decade as a permanent secretary. His portfolio includes non-executive directorships with the Financial Reporting Council and Pool Re, and as a trustee of Lloyds Register Foundation.

595 Bertrand De Mazieres
DG Finance
European Investment Bank

Bertrand De Mazieres is also on the board of ICMA.

596 Clifford Lewis
NED
Eurex Clearing

Cliff Lewis sits on the board of EUREX Clearing and has worked all over the parish including at the Chicago Board of Trade. From 2001 to 2013, he was CEO of Currenex. He is currently a NED of Eris Exchange and member of the CFTC Technology Advisory Committee.

597 Kathleen Tyson
CEO
Granularity

Kathleen Tyson is a go-to person if, say you want a small securities lending entity or other financial market infrastructure knocked up without much hassle, or stress. In her spare time, an accomplished medieval historian.

598 Steffen Koehler
COO
EEX

Steffen Koehler is a EUREX Clearing alumni who has made the move to the dynamic EEX entity, most recently as COO.

599 Chew Sutat
EVP Head of Equities & Fixed Income
SGX

Chew Sutat has been an EVP at SGX since 2007, having previously worked for several of the leading banks in Singapore.

600 Wataru Ito
Senior MD
TFX

Wataru Ito is Senior MD at TFX, one of the most exciting markets...once we see an end to Jaoan's remarkable QE.

601-625

601 Mark Makepeace
CEO FTSE & Group Dir Information Services
LSEG

The long-time FTSE boss Mark Makepeace has even been making deals of his own volition of late in index acquisition (Citi Bond indices, May 2017). Could he yet vault to a staggering degree in the LSE hierarchy? Some internal gossip suggests he might be in with a chance of succeeding Xavier Rolet.

602 Kenneth Bertsch
Executive Director
Council of Institutional Investors (US)

As executive director at the Council of Institutional Investors (US) Kenneth Bertsch has acute influence in the developing issue of multi class shares and voting rights or lack thereof which has become especially acute as the latest wave of silicon valley empires come to market often bereft of shareholder democracy.

603 Thomas Dierkes
MD
Boerse Duesseldorf

Thomas Dierkes is MD of Boerse Dusseldorf.

604 David Grayson
Co-Founder & CEO
Auerbach Grayson & Company

David Grayson is co-founder and CEO of Auerbach Grayson & Company, a global broker with reach into 125 countries worldwide. He thus retains an interest in many areas of the parish!

605 Elzbieta Bienkowska
DG Competition & Entrepreneurship
EC

As DG Competition and Entrepreneurship, Elzbieta Bienkowska oversees a portfolio which must deliver its part of CMU if the Euro is to survive and if the EU is to prosper.

606 Ben Bucknell
CEO
OnMarketBookBuilds

A former lawyer and Macquarie staffer, Ben Bucknell is CEO of OnMarket BookBuilds and has extensive experience in investment banking, private equity, and corporate law. He is also the only person in the EI100 to have previously worked as a pearl diver (with Australia's Paspaley Pearls).

607 Anthony Robson
CEO
Yieldbroker

Anthony Robson was appointed and started work as CEO of Australia's SEF on May 3rd 2017 replacing longstanding CEO Richard Swift.

608 Matteo Andreetto
CEO
STOXX

Matteo Andreetto has been head of STOXX since 2016, and is on a self-proclaimed mission to innovate...no bad thing for DB1 – let's hope he can.

609 Mathew Kuppe
MD
360T Asia Pacific

Mathew Kuppe is a founding partner, member of the Group Executive Board and managing director for 360T Asia Pacific Pte Ltd, a position he has held since December 2006 when he opened up the company's regional headquarters in Singapore.

610 Andrew Dyson
CEO
ISLA

In July 2016 Andy Dyson was promoted to CEO, having joined as the COO of the International Securities Lending Association in 2013. His previous role was EMEA Director Specialist Sales & Head of Account Management at Data Explorers (now Markit).

611 Matthias Graulich
Member of the Exec Committee
Eurex Clearing

Matthias Graulich has been with DB1 since 2001 and on the board of EUREX Clearing since 2014.

612 Abdulrahman M. Al Mofadhi
Vice Chairman
Tadawul

Abdulrahman Al Mofadhi is currently the Acting Secretary General of the Public Investment Fund of Saudi Arabia and a board member of the National Commercial Bank, chairman of the Board of Directors of Alakaria and Bahri Companies. In addition, he served as an executive director of the world Bank Group. In the parish he is deputy chairman of Tadawul.

613 Sallie Krawcheck
CEO
Ellevest
NED at DAH

A longstanding Wall Street player, Sallie Krawcheck is of pertinence to the parish through her board position at Digital Asset Holdings.

614 Satyanarayan Goel
CEO
Indian Energy Exchange

N. Goel has been CEO of IEX since 2014 and is now moving the company towards an IPO in the near future as India's dominant power exchange looks to the future.

615 Mark Wetjen
MD
Global Policy
DTCC

Former CFTC Commissioner Mark Wetjen is MD for global policy of DTCC.

616 Arminta Saladziene
Head of Securities Services Baltic/Nordic
NASDAQ

Arminta Saladziene is VP, head of securities services and chairman of broker services across the Baltic and Nordic regions for NASDAQ as well as being responsible for the Vilnius exchange.

617 Sanjit Prasad
CEO
Indian Commodity Exchange (ICEX)

It is unclear quite what ICEX will look like in a year but it ought to be different!

At present Reliance Capital holds 26% stake in the exchange, while other stakeholders include MMTC, Indian Potash, Kribhco, and IDFC Bank. Sanjit Prasad is engineering a deal to merge with NMCE while in its own right ICEX recently received the green light to restart their commodity exchange.

618 Ms Nurhaida
CEO of Capital Market Supervision
Indonesia Financial Services Authority
IOSCO Member of the Board

Ms Nurhaida heads capital market supervision at the Indonesian regulator as well as being a member of the IOSCO board.

619 Ashok Sinha
Chairman
Indian Commodity Exchange (ICEX)

Ashok Sinha is chairman of ICEX which is seeking to merge with NMCE to create the third largest Indian commodity exchange behind MCX and NCDEX.

620 Tom Bendixen
GC
Cinnober

Tom Bendixen has 30 years of experience in the exchange industry, joining Cinnober in 2016 from his previous position at Eurex/Deutsche Börse, where he was responsible for exchange cooperation. His duties at DB1 included representation in working committees of WFE, as well as sitting on the board of GMEX Group and the Bombay SE.

621 Sir John W. Gieve
NED
CLS

Sir John Gieve served as Deputy Governor of the Bank of England from January 2006 until February 2009 and is currently a non-executive director of ILS.

622 Martin Moloney
Head of Markets Policy Division
Central Bank of Ireland
IOSCO Member of the Board

Martin Moloney Head of Markets Policy Division at the Central Bank of Ireland, Ireland, sits on the IOSCO board.

623 Egbert Laege
CEO
Powernext
Europex Member of the Board, Europex General Assembly

Egbert Laege runs Powernext and is on the EUROPEX board.

624 Richard Gorelick
Co-Founder & CEO
RGM

Richard Gorelick runs RGM, a major player in prop trading around the world which was acquired by DRW operated by Don Wilson (381) just as we closed for press in late August 2017.

625 Jon Moulton
Chairman
The International Stock Exchange (TISE)

Jon Moulton is a de facto household name in British private equity.

Moulton is the founder and managing partner of the private equity firm Better Capital, having formerly been the managing partner of the UK private equity firm Alchemy Partners. Nowadays in the parish he sits as chairman of the Channel Islands Stock Exchange which renamed itself the International Stock Exchange earlier in 2017.

626-650

626 Mikael Lundin
CEO
Nord Pool
Europex Member of the Board, Europex General Assembly

Mikael Lundin runs Nordpool and is a Member of the Europex board.

627 Anil Stocker
CEO
MarketInvoice

Anil Stocker cofounded MarketInvoice in 2011 and has run the business ever since, in the process creating a veritable powerhouse of invoice financing in the UK.

628 Jurg Spillmann
Member of the Board
Eurex

Jurg Spillmann was re-elected as a Member of the Board, Eurex Zurich AG in June 2017 and it is good that they retain his wise counsel. The former CTO was a key member of the team which made EUREX a world class player, dragging the more recalcitrant cash markets of DB1 with them. Jurg's quiet but highly coherent thinking is the sort of considered management approach much missed day to day at the top of the modern DB1 apparatus.

629 Amnon Neubach
Chairman
TASE

Amnon Neubach has proven a controversial chairman of TASE and it appears his power is now on the wane with the appointment of a new CEO.

630 Bill Baxter
Head of Global Program Trading &
Market Structure Fidelity

Bill Baxter sits on the advisory board of Luminex and has long been a thinker in the execution space for buyside fund managers.

631 Martin Abbott
CEO
NFEX Markets

Martin Abbott is back in the metals arena looking to compete with the incumbents and as we closed for press, perhaps using the LME CCP.

632 M. Shaifur Rahman Mazumdar
MD
Chittagong Stock Exchange

The Chittagong SE MD M. Shaifur Rahman Mazumdar hits the headlines as this publication headed to press, proposing an investment by the Chinese shareholder group in Pakistan SE in the Bangladesh market.

633 VJ Angelo
CEO
LondonDX

VJ Angelo runs the London DX although his most recent headline moment was an unfortunate motorcycle accident from which, thankfully, he is now recovering.

634 Bjorn Sibbern
EVP Global Information Services
NASDAQ

Bjorn Sibbern is executive vice president for Global Information Services at NASDAQ. In this role he is responsible for the strategic direction and overseeing all aspects of the company's Index and Data Products businesses which provide solutions, intelligence and insight to the global capital markets.

635 Nikolaj Kosakewitsch
Head of Copenhagen SE
NASDAQ

In his new role as president of NASDAQ Copenhagen, Nikolaj Kosakewitsch also has the functional position as head of sales for NASDAQ European Equities, having joined NASDAQ from Carnegie in June 2017.

636 A.K. Abdul Momen
Chairman
Chittagong Stock Exchange

Abdul Momen, chairman of Chittagong SE is a former ambassador and permanent representative of Bangladesh to the United Nations.

637 Phil Bruce
Member of the Board
ICE Futures Europe

Phil Bruce, veteran of LIFFE, LCH and LSE is nowadays an influential guiding presence on the board of ICE Futures Europe

638 Kristian Schach Moller
CEO
Ace Africa

Kristian Schach Moller runs one of those fascinating if little heard of exchanges, the ACE which is seeking to help Africa grow its commodity markets in an orderly fashion.

639 Jane Diplock AO
NED
SGX

Jane Diplock AO is a non-executive director of SGX and chairman of the Abu Dhabi Global Market Regulatory Committee as well as serving on international advisory boards to SEBI in India and CSRC in China.

640 Paul Chou
CEO & Co-Founder
LedgerX

CEO and co-founder of LedgerX, Paul Chou, was finally delivered the potential to make hay with his entity being regulated by the CFTC just days before this listing closed for press. Very interesting times for LedgerX. Chou may be poised to rocket up this list in the next 12 months.

641 Roel Campos
NED
Liquidnet

A former SEC Commissioner Roel Campos, was perceived as being particularly beneficial to Liquidnet when they found themselves in difficulty with the SEC a few years back.

642 Mehrdad Nemati
Chairman
Iran Fara Bourse

Mehrdad Nemati is chairman of the Iran Fara Borse (OTC market).

643 Maureen O'Hara
Robert W. Purcell Professor of Finance
Cornell University's Johnson Graduate School of Management
SEC Market Structure Committee Member

Maureen O'Hara is a former ITG chairman, with various board positions in times past including the Sebi India global advisory board. She currently sits on the SEC Market Structure Committee.

644 Soren Martens
MD
Fish Pool

Soren Martens is MD of Fish pool. He has spent 20 years working in the fish industry and its transportation.

645 Sri Subrato Das
CEO
Calcutta Stock Exchange

Exchange Invest applauds the efforts of Calcutta SE to survive against the over-arching fiat of SEBI which is trying to impose a national market structure which will be to the detriment of a dynamic digital India.

646 Akhilesh Awasthy
SVP
Indian Energy Exchange
APEx Member of the Board

IEX SVP Akhilesh Awasthy is also on the board of APeX.

647 Dan Thieke
MD
DTCC
ACSDA Executive Committee Member

Dan Thieke is an MD at DTCC and a board member of ACSDA.

648 Will Mitting
Publisher
FOW

Will Mitting does a good job within Euromoney promoting the derivatives business line through what has now been rebranded Global Investor Group, formerly FOW.

649 Richard Seaman
Chairman
Xactium

Richard Seaman is one of the 'eminence grise' figures in derivatives regulation. Based in the UK but with a global reach across markets.

650 Marcelo Wilk
Director of CSD
B3

Marcelo Wilk is the director of the CSD at B3 and a former ACSDA Executive Committee Member.

651-675

651 Paul Humphrey
Head of FICC
Euronext

As Head of FICC Paul Humphrey looks like a riser in next year's index as the recent acquisitions of FastMatch and the Algomi partnership, to name but two deals, provide him with significant optionality to grow Euronext.

652 Muneer Kamal
Chairman
Pakistan Stock Exchange (PSX)

Muneer Kamal has extensive experience in Pakistan across multiple banks and now serves as chairman of the recently listed Pakistan Stock Exchange which was created unifying the Pakistani regional exchanges into one megabourse. Nominated by the SECP he was appointed chairman of the reconstituted board including the Chinese minority shareholders who invested in a 40% stake in the exchange earlier in 2017.

653 Sven Giegold
MEP
EU

A former anti-globalisation activist turned Green MEP who is at the epicentre of moves to reform (i.e. raise) tax in the EU. He was a co-founder of the International Tax Justice Network which, as the catchy name implies in this era, is aimed at higher taxes to the point of economic illiteracy. An economist (apparently) but not a coherent supporter of markets. Mr Giegold is influential for his toxic potential amongst the too often navel gazing student politics of the European Parliament.

654 Chris Richardson
CEO
Percival Software

Chris Richardson is the man you may never have heard of, until you want to buy a CSD system. Percival is the system of choice at present in many markets across the world.

655 Sri Bhaskar Sen
Chairman
Calcutta Stock Exchange

Currently battling the SEBI diktats which seek a couple of national markets in what is an absurd failure of market understanding.

656 Huseyin Erkan
Advisor to the Board of Commissioners
Capital Market Authority (CMA)

Huseyin Erkan is currently Advisor to the Board of Commissioners at CMA, Riyadh, having been WFE CEO and prior to that CEO of the Istanbul Stock Exchange. He remains a popular urbane figure in the parish.

657 David Feltes
Market Infrastructure Consultant
KPMG

Dave was the COO taken for granted in CME Europe who has been around the parish for countless years with experience from multiple perspectives. Now demonstrating his consulting skills once again via the good offices of KPMG.

658 Lukas Petrikas
VP Group Strategy
HKEX

Waking up in the morning is not believed to be difficult for Lukas Petrikas as his position overseeing Group Strategy for HKEX is akin to the most stunning jigsaw of opportunity overlaid with a fabulous set of Mahjong layered jade-encrusted...okay you get the picture.

659 Jignesh Shah
Chairman Emeritus
FTIL (now 63moons)

Not actually a member of the formal leadership team at FTIL but is hard to believe much goes on without his imprimatur. Last seen crying conspiracy at all who would listen as the latest wave of accusations concerning the NSEL fiasco were aimed at him and others as the EI1000 closed for press. Clearly in the past Jignesh Shah would have been a leading parish player in influence but those days now look long gone.

660 Lumintang Paulus
President
Jakarta Futures Exchange

Lumintang Paulus is president director of the Jakarta Futures Exchange.

661 Justice Siddiqur Rahman Miah
Director
Dhaka Stock Exchange

A Justice of the Appellate Division, Bangladesh Supreme Court, Siddiqur Rahman Miah stood down as chairman but remains a board member.

662 Enoch Yiu
Journalist
SCMP

As Chief Reporter for Business in the South China Morning Post, Enoch Yiu has a diverse portfolio but she deftly manages to balance a lot of discussion in the exchange and regulatory arenas as it impacts Hong Kong whether purely within the islands, across mainland issues, or internationally.

663 Mansour Yazdizadeh
Chairman
Iran Mercantile Exchange

Mansour Yazdizadeh chairs the Iran Mercantile Exchange and is a director of Esfahan Steel.

664 Pedro Zorrilla
AGD Corporate Services & Institutional Relations
Bolsa Mexicana de Valores
FIAB Vice-President

Pedro Zorrilla is FIAB VP and at the Mexican bourse, he is AGD Corporate Services and Institutional Relations.

665 Paul Pickup
CEO
Trading Technology

Paul Pickup remains a leading figure in the implementation, development and upkeep of exchange systems across the world with decades of front line experience.

666 Andrew Simpson
Head of Post Trade
Euronext

Andrew Simpson runs the post trade operations of Euronext from London.

667 Tom Krantz
Senior Advisor Capital Markets
Thomas Murray

Tom Krantz was formerly the head of the WFE before that organisation took a funny turn - or perhaps just took itself too seriously. That was back in the day when Duncan Niederauer could turn most everything he touched to stone. Nowadays Tom is enjoying life with the good folks of Thomas Murray as a senior advisor in all aspects of capital markets including post trade.

668 G M Campbell
Chairman
Baltic Exchange

Chairman Campbell oversaw the sale to SGX.

669 Hamed Soltaninejad
CEO
Iran Mercantile Exchange

Hamed Soltaninejad is CEO of the fabulously diverse Iran Mercantile Exchange which will soon be selling new cars as part of its broad array of products from agriculture to metals to gold coins and more!

670 Pedro J. Mejia Gomez
Chairman & CEO OMIE & OMIP
Europex member of the Board, Europex General Assembly

Pedro J. Mejia Gomez is chairman & CEO of the Portuguese electricity market and serves on the EUROPEX board.

671 Javier Jara Traub
Business & Legal Manager
DCV
ACSDA Executive Committee Member

Chilean CSD staffer Javier Jara Traub is also on the executive committee of the ACSDA.

672 Andreas Gustafsson
Chairman Nasdaq Sweden
NASDAQ

Andreas Gustafsson is senior vice president/Chief Counsel Europe NASDAQ as well as chairman of NASDAQ Stockholm.

673 Richard Balarkas
Member of the Board
BATS Europe

One of the original titans of Europe's MTF revolution as Instinent CEO, Richard Balarkas is a member of the BATS board, the Saxo Capital Markets Board and a director of the FIX committee amongst other appointments.

674 David Cummings
Chairman
Tradebot

David Cummings of Tradebot built the original ECN called BATS. One line doesn't do him justice, a book would be just about sufficient.

675 Jorge Alegria
Consultant
Financial Market Advisory

Jorge Alegria was formerly head of the Mexican exchange's derivatives arm MEXDer and is currently an advisor to the president of CME Clearing and a member of the board of Goldman Sachs Mexico.

676-700

676 Padraic O'Connor
Chairman Irish Stock Exchange
NED European Wholesale Securities Market

The Irish Stock Exchange chairman is also on the board of the EWSM JV between the Irish SE and the Malta SE.

677 Tomas Carruthers
CEO
Social Stock Exchange

Tomas Carruthers has been pushing the Social Stock Exchange with some gusto - and not a little (presumably environmentally friendly) gin over the years.

678 Hugh Simpson
Senior Partner
Bourse Consult

Hugh Simpson is unlikely to find himself with much time on his hands despite the closure of CME Europe where he held a board position. The former Crest CEO and Euroclear executive is usually in considerable demand around the world.

679 Nigel Cairns
GM
LSEG Technology

Nigel Cairns now has responsibility for Millennium IT alongside other LSEG products. The new LSEG Technology brand may mark a renaissance in efforts to sell the LSEG exchange technology but it may also represent a retrenchment away from the parish milieu of matching engines et al given the highly competitive current environment.

680 Bart Chilton
Senior Policy Advisor
DLA

Former CFTC Commissioner Bart Chilton is always colourful and opinionated even if currently he is frustrated to see much of his work at CFTC possibly heading into a deregulatory wave fuelled by the Trump Presidency.

681 Wojciech Nagel
Chairman
Warsaw SE

Wojciech Nagel chairs the WSE which has been vastly diminished in parish influence by the endless interventions from consecutive governments of recent years.

682 Joe Bannister
Chairman
MFSA

Professor Joseph "Joe" Bannister enjoyed a spectacular H1 2017 as the Maltese EU Presidency demonstrated remarkable dynamism and under Finance Minister Scicluna's input, an excellent series of dossier achievements. Perhaps slated for retirement by the end of 2017, Professor Bannister deserves plaudits for hitting hugely above Malta's weight over the years with the Presidency a high water mark for his remarkable career as the MFSA chairman building the organisation from scratch.

683 Yu-Ching Su
CEO
Taipei Exchange (GreTai Securities Market)

Yu-Ching Su runs the Taipei OTC market which incidentally recently signed an MOU with Ivana Gazic of Zagreb Exchange in Taipei to help grow the Croatian stock market.

684 Philip Chen
Chairman
Taipei Exchange (GreTai Securities Market)

Philip Chen is chairman of the remarkable TaiPei Exchange which runs the gamut of startup through SME funding into listing.

685 Mehdi Mohammad Esmaeil Fadaei Nezhad
Chairman Tehran Stock Exchange

Mehdi Mohammad Esmaeil Fadaei Nezhad chairs the Tehran SE.

686 Daniel Coleman
CEO
KCG Holdings
Member of SIFMA board

On the board of SIFMA as well as heading KCG but imminently headed for departure...now on his gardening leave as the deal closed and the EI1000 also closed for press.

687 James Eric Barr
Chairman
Sydney Stock Exchange

688 Nick Motteram
MD
OnMarketBookBuilds

Nick Motteram guides companies through their book building process from his position as MD at the innovative OnMarketBookBuilds company based in Sydney, Australia.

689 Lynton Jones
Chairman Emeritus
Bourse Consult

Former OM LX, IPE and Jiway boss who co founded Bourse Consult and has held various board positions in Europe and the Middle East.

690 Jeff Mehan
CEO
TFS Americas &
Tradition SEF
WMBA Americas Member of the Board

Jeff Mehan also sits on the WMBA board.

691 Gerald Corcoran
R.J. O'Brien & Associates
FIA Member of the Board

Corcoran sits on the FIA board.

692 Daiga Auzina-Melalksne
Chairman
NASDAQ Latvia

Daiga Auzina-Melalksne is Chairman of NASDAQ Latvia.

693 Sanjay Arya
Global Head of Indexes
Morningstar

Sanjay Arya is the global head of indices at MorningStar.

694 Peter Cox
Co-Founder
Bourse Consult

A former OM LX boss and long-time advisor to Cinnober, Peter is a popular figure in the parish.

695 Mark Yallop
NED PRA
Chairman FICC Market Standard Board

696 Indars Ascuks
Deputy Chairman
NASDAQ Riga
ECSDA Executive Committee member

A leading figure in the Baltic exchanges and CSDs, with a seat on the ECSDA executive committee, Indars remains active also through FESE.

697 Stu Taylor
CEO
Algomi

Algomi founder Stu Taylor has various interesting opportunities ahead including his deal with Euronext.

698 Bill Herder
Head of Asia Pacific
FIA

Bill Herder heads the FIA operations in Asia Pacific and sits on the board of Bursa Malaysia's derivatives subsidiary.

699 Jamie Khurshid
CEO
Boat

Jamie has been pushing the Boat franchise to new tides under Cinnober's ownership.

700 David Setters
Dude Philanthropist & Consultant
All manner of Good Ventures Especially MiND

Dave has been essentially omnipresent in the derivatives end of the parish for so long that he probably remembers when Leo Melamed was a young thing. A former MD of FOW and currently a partner of consultancy Contango Markets, David has been working tirelessly to raise funds for Motor Neuron Disease research to seek a cure which will help those in the next generation who might suffer the diagnosis he cruelly received in 2011. In what is a perfect tribute to any proper Englishman, he has a City of London cricket cup named after him – who wouldn't feel proud to be so honoured?

701-725

701 Phil Bird
CEO
Perfect Channel

Through his unique specialist enterprise, Perfect Channel, Phil has created the biggest knowledge base on auctions of any vendor.

702= Michelle Janke
MD
STT

702 = Louisjan Bonthuys
Operations Director
STT

703 Joe Cassidy
Partner - Global Market Infrastructure
KPMG

Joe Cassidy has had a lot on his plate with Brexit work this past year and continues to advise on multiple elements of capital market structure.

704 Mats Wilhelmsson
CEO
Hemso 180 Konsult

Mats was a co-founder of Scila and remains a leading expert in surveillance systems.

705 Jake Pugh
Thinker & Game Changer
Independent

One of the tangibly useful consultants in the parish who has been in the background on several key projects of late, making it difficult to avoid including Jake just on the basis of number of airports he was spotted in heading off to see clients on different continents.

706 Gottfried Steiner
CEO & Chairman
CEGH
Europex General Assembly

Gottfried Steiner runs the Vienna Boerse's electricity & gas exchange subsidiary.

707 Henri Bergstrom
Advisor for Business Development
Abu Dhabi Securities Exchange

Formerly Head of NASDAQ Global Post Trade Solutions and chairman of NASDAQ Armenia, Henri Bergstrom became Advisor for Business Development at the Abu Dhabi Securities Exchange just as this index went to press.

708 Jeff Lynn
Executive Chairman
Seedrs

Jeff Lynn has helped make equity crowdfunding hugely popular in the UK through his Seedrs platform. It was confirmed 11th August in Exchange Invest, he is moving to become Executive Chairman with the filling of the CEO position at Seedrs through promotion of COO Jeff Kelisky after an 18-month search.

709 Sheila Bair
President
Washington College
Thomson Reuters NED

710 Stuart Turner Founder & Director
Avenir Technology
NED TISE

With Avenir finding its latest client in the Lebanon for a CCP, Stuart's software distributed through GMEX is finding a new audience. Also a board member of TISE (formerly the Channel Islands Stock Exchange).

711 Monica Singer
CEO
Strate

Monica Singer is a veteran of the Johannesburg SE CSD.

712 Brigitte Daurelle
CEO
Euroclear France
ECSDA Vice-Chairman

Brigitte Daurelle is ECSDA vice chairman and boss of Euroclear France.

713 Fernando Canas Berkowitz
President
Bolsa Electronica de Chile

President of Bolsa Chile.

714 Richard Korhammer
Chairman
Yieldbroker

715 Juan Carlos Spencer Ossa
GM
Bolsa Electronica de Chile

716 David Clark
Chairman
Wholesale Markets Brokers Association (Europe)

A lifelong city staffer, who also served on the board of TP ICAP, David Clark has been Chairman of WMBA for some time pushing the case for the IDB association in Europe from London.

717 Silvio Brkic
CEO
CROPEX
Europex General Assembly

718 Holger Wohlenberg
Chairman
STOXX

719 Rob Boardman
CEO Europe
ITG

As boss of the ITG Europe franchise, at least Rob is far away from the scandals which engulfed his US colleagues at HQ. Good algo business but clearly ITG must be concerned about the explosive debut of BATS BIDS LiS.

720 Richard Redding
CEO
Index Industry Association

An industry veteran who heads the small but pertinent Index Association.

721 Adam Kostyal
SVP Listings Europe
NASDAQ

Adam appears to have made the move smoothly from selling the OMX / NASDAQ software platforms to becoming head of listings for Europe within a NASDAQ where in particular the SME markets have been on fire of late.

722 Matt Dolton
CEO
Kynetix

Matt Dolton is the co-founder and recently appointed CEO of Kynetix (fellow co-founder CEO Paul Smyth stepped down to become non-exec chairman). Matt was responsible for identifying the niche Kynetix had carved out in understanding the complexities of exchange-based physical commodity trading. Having been instrumental in winning business with LIFFE and LME, Matt steered the business to invest in building out the market infrastructure platform now known as Sentinel – an ecosystem that digitises commodities and connects the financial and physical markets.

Under Matt's stewardship, Kynetix have been successful in winning new business with commodity exchanges who aim to bring security to assets in storage – helping eliminate fraud, build trust and encourage financial players to bring liquidity to commodity markets with greater ease and certainty.

723 Vittorio Conti
President
Hi-MTF

Former CONSOB Commissioner Vittorio Conti runs Hi-MTF, a Milan-based platform offering a variety of financial instruments such as corporate bonds, banks, high yield, structured debt and emerging market bonds.

724 Markus Schuler
Head Of Regulatory Affairs & Market Structure
Tradeweb

Long influential in the EU lobbying circle, Marcus heads regulatory affairs and market structure for Markit IHS in London.

725 Milan Bozic
CEO
Banja Luka SE

Milan heads an exchange which has already enjoyed a colourful history despite its short lifespan. Created in the rump Bosnian Serb statelet, like the economy itself Banja Luka had to battle to survive but it has thrived and prospered thanks to the dynamism of Milan's leadership.

726-750

726 Bob Antell
Executive Chairman
KB Tech

A longstanding parish data expert with a wealth of experience in commodities and technology dating back to the LCE and beyond! Under Bob's chairmanship, KB Tech has managed not merely to supply to the likes of ClearTrade but also EEX which acquired the Singapore based market in April 2016.

727 Julie Lerner
Founder & CEO
PanXchange

Julie Lerner sees riches in the wealth of African commodities through building markets and platforms – it's a difficult path but the potential remains enormous.

728 Boris Tomaz Snuderl
CEO
KDD
ECSDA Executive Committee member

Boris runs the well managed, independently owned Slovenian depositary while sitting on the ECSDA executive committee.

729 Peter Fredriksson
CEO
Baymarkets Technology

Having suffered a few health issues, Peter was less prominent in the parish until his return recently. Principal of Baymarkets, an innovative supplier which emerged from the remarkable tech cluster first built by OMX around Stockholm.

730 Anthony Tassone
Founder & Chief Product Officer
GreenKey

Anthony Tassone stood down as CEO of GreenKey in early 2016 which he founded to become chief product officer.

731 David Walker
Chairman SETL
also Chairman Winton Capital

Chairman of SETL after a simply stellar City of London career, he is also chairman of David Harding's Winton Capital hedge fund.

732 Jim Falvey
EVP & GC
NYSD

A former ICE GC, Jim Falvey nowadays has a fascinating portfolio of interests including NYSD, the parent of Clearable.

733 Fariz Azizov
Chairman
Baku SE

Fariz Azizov chairs the supervisory board of Baku SE. Having been appointed managing director at Compulsory Insurance Bureau in December 2016 he was elevated to supervisory board chairman having previously been president of the Management Board (AKA CEO).

734 Vugar Namazov
CEO
Baku SE

Vugar Namazov has worked his way through the ranks of the Baku SE and was acting CEO (president of the Management Board) until being made permanent in June 2017.

735 KAM Majedur Rahman
MD
Dhaka Stock Exchange

KAM Majedur Rahman is MD of Dhaka SE which this year joined the WFE.

736 David Kucera
Secretary General
PXE
Europex General Assembly

David Kucera is secretary general of the Prague Energy Exchange and a member of the EUROPEX General Assembly.

737 Jill Sommers
Senior Advisor
Patomak

Former CFTC Commissioner Jill Sommers is a Member of the Board and audit committee chairman of BATS, advisory board member of Green Key Technologies and serves as a senior advisor to Patomak.

738 Peter Maragos
CEO
Dash

Peter Maragos has had an eventful year. On January 4th 2017, Dash announced that it was acquiring LiquidPoint, the options trading and technology business of Convergex.

739 Hossein Fahimi
Chairman
CSD Iran

Dr Hossein Fahimi is chairman of CSD Iran, having been appointed in August 2016.

740 Nick Cowan
CEO
Gibraltar SE

Nick Cowan is CEO of Gibraltar SE which sits right on the doorstep to Europe but is outside the EU. A fascinating position given recent suicide notes for bond issuers to emanate from the EU's regulatory authorities. Moreover as we closed for press the Gibraltar SE announced it was intending to trailblazer in the delivery of Blockchain technology on the exchange.

741 Mohamed Salman
CEO
Erbil SE

Mohamed Salman is CEO of the Kurdistan SE in Erbil which was first created in 2013.

742 Jim Northey
Consultant
Itiviti

Longstanding leading figure in the FIX community whose work with all manner of exchanges and vendors leaves him well respected on both sides of the Atlantic.

743 Carl Monroe
Southwest Power Pool (USA)
APEx Member of the Board

744 Aliyev Araz Ismayil Oglu
Chairman
ETS

Aliyev Araz Ismayil Oglu is chairman of the Eurasian Trade System Commodity Exchange (ETS) in Almaty, Kazakhstan, a 60/40 jv between Regional Financial Center of Almaty (RFCA) and RTS Stock Exchange OJSC.

745 David Ewasuik
CEO
Market Evolution

David Ewasuik, one of several Alberta Market Solutions veterans on the EI1000 runs Market Evolution Software which supplies a series of markets with exchange and CSD solutions across the world. He also sits on the Advisory board of the Bermuda Stock Exchange.

746 Suma Chakrabarti
President
EBRD

Formerly Britain's most senior civil servant, Indian born Sir Suma Chakrabarti, in West Bengal, India, is the sixth President of the European Bank for Reconstruction nd Development (EBRD) having succeeded Thomas Mirow in 2012 and being re-elected by the Board of Governors for a second 4 year term in 2016.

747 Matt Levine
Columnist
Bloomberg View

Not a direct media parishioner but his interventions on market structure topics are well considered and always very readable.

748 Alberto A. Padoan
President
Rosario Board of Trade

Alberto A. Padoan is chairman of the Rosario Board of Trade (BCR) in the Argentine city, with a focus on agriculture.

749 Mohammed Habibus Samad
CEO
Central Depository Bangladesh
Member of the Board SAFE

750 Ludovic Aigrot
VP European Affairs
NASDAQ

Ludovic heads Nasdaq's European Office of Government Relations in Brussels and he maintains close relations with FESE, EACH and WFE on regulatory matters as well as the EU/EC bodies themselves. Formerly Director of EU Affairs for Euronext, he also worked at the Council of Europe on economic crime issues as well as for the French derivatives market (MATIF) and in the banking sector.

751-775

751 Professor Dr Abul Hashem
Chairman
Dhaka Stock Exchange

Professor Dr Abul Hashem became chairman of Dhaka SE in February 2017. He is professor of the Dhaka University Accounting and Information Communication Department and was elected recently vice chancellor of the University of Scholars.

752 Ivan Steriev
CEO
Macedonian SE

The Macedonian SE CEO Ivan Steriev was a co-founder of the SEELink project unifying access to exchanges across the SEE region.

753 Mahmut Kayacik
CEO
Istanbul Settlement and Custody Bank

Mahmut Kayacik runs TakasBank, the subsidiary of BIST, which makes much of the money thanks to its control of repo trading/clearing etc.

754 Gojko Maksimovic
CEO
Montenegro SE

Gojko Maksimovic has been CEO of the Montenegro SE for almost four and a half years as we close for press and was instrumental in arranging their investment from Borsa Istanbul.

755 Ray Abeywardena
Chairman
Colombo Stock Exchange

Ray Abeywardena has ambitious plans for Colombo SE and is looking forward to a wave of new content from government privatisation of State Owned Enterprises.

756 Ivan O'Toole
Sales Director
Perfect Channel

A thinker with considerable expertise across the nutty issues of trading all manner of markets, Ivan O'Toole is thriving within the Perfect Channel organisation, bringing to life the ability to deliver any form of auction as a service to best deliver pricing in commodities, regardless of their specific peculiarities.

757 Mostafa Haghighi Mehmandari
Chairman Securities Exchange Brokers Association of Iran (SEBA)

Mostafa Haghighi Mehmandari is chairman of the Securities Exchange Brokers Association of Iran.

758 Max Bowie
Editor
Inside Data Management

Does a simply brilliant job bringing alive a lot of tenets to the market data picture with colour. A tough task at the best of times, Max Bowie is a leading trade journalist whose focus has paid off through his excellent content.

759 Juan A. Estrada
CEO
Mercado Abierto Electronico

Executive director of the MAE since 2015, Juan A. Estrada oversees the leading Argentine market in government and private fixed-income securities, foreign currencies and swaps as well as currency and interest rate futures.

760 Khalil Nasser
CEO
Securities Depositary of Jordan (SDC)

Khalil Nasser has been CEO of the Jordanian CSD in an acting and then permanent capacity since 2015.

761 Lucian-Claudiu Anghel
Chairman
Bucharest Stock Exchange

Anghel seems to have managed to make the tiresomely fractious politics of the Bucharest Stock Exchange a little more calm in recent years albeit the structural problems of Romania's cowboy capitalism remain.

762 Luis Ribaya
Chairman
Mercado Abierto Electronico

Involved with MAE since its inception, Dr Luis Ribaya is an attorney-at-law, and was appointed chairman of MAE in 2003.

763 Mourad Ben Chaabane
Chairman
Bourse de Tunis

Mourad Ben Chaabane was elected chairman of the Tunis SE in May 2017. He has been the DG of MAC SA for 20 years.

764 Simon Brickles
Chairman
Capital Access Group

Father of AIM, former CEO of Plus and still in many ways the 'go to' figure in European SME exchanges.

765 Jaroslaw Ziebiec
Director Regulated Market Development Office
PolPX

Polish exchange veteran Jaroslaw Ziebiec benefitted from his sojourn to London working for Bloomberg when he left GPW due to his testy relationship with then CEO Ludwik Sobolewski.

766 Talat Ulussever
CEO & Deputy Chairman
EPIAS
Europex General Assembly

Talat Ulussever is CEO and deputy chairman of EPIAS, the Turkish power exchange.

767 Rajeeva Bandaranaike
CEO
Colombo Stock Exchange

Rajeeva Bandaranaike became CEO of the Colombo SE in 2013.

768 Ron Bernstein
Augment Partners

A former leading options market maker in New York, Ron ran GSX/Intrade as its original CEO and has maintained a close watch on the prediction market space ever since. A very early blockchain adopter, he is closely involved with the Augur prediction markets venture.

769 Brian Tembo
CEO
Lusaka Stock Exchange

Brian Tembo has been CEO of the Lusaka SE since 2013 and is a former member of the Executive Committee of ASEA.

770 Taha Ahmed Al-Rubaye
CEO
Iraq Stock Exchange

Taha Ahmed Al-Rubaye is CEO of the Iraq Stock Exchange.

771 Olga Cantillo
CEO
Bolsa de Valores de Panama
ACSDA Treasurer

Olga Cantillo has a long career in banking behind her and has been EVP and DG of the Panama SE since 2015.

772 Nayan Mehta
CFO
Bombay Stock Exchange
Senior Vice Chairman SAFE

Nayan Mehta is CFO of Bombay SE and senior vice chairman of SAFE.

773 Efrain Diego Carvajal
General Counsel Caja De Valores (Argentina)
ACSDA Executive Committee Member

Efrain Diego Carvajal is a member of the executive committee of the Argentine CSD and an ACSDA Executive Committee Member.

774 Joseph Portelli
Chairman
Malta Stock Exchange

Joe Portelli has been vastly more innovative in his thinking than his modest stipend as Malta SE chairman would suggest is a viable ratio of input to income! Created the very ambitious Maltese National Capital Markets Action Plan and is in the process of introducing over 20 steps to radically rework not merely the Malta SE itself but also the Maltese financial centre with it.

775 Gabriele Frediani
Chief Biz Dev Officer
Elixium

Once encountered never forgotten. A lifelong bond market guru. Mostly harmless.

776-800

776 The Rt. Hon. The Lord Hague Of Richmond
Chairman
ICE Futures Europe

A serious player in UK political circles despite his retirement from government before the 2015 general election, Lord Hague is now leading the ICE Europe board filling in the shoes of the legendary Sir Bob Reid.

777 Emma Shand
Chairman
NASDAQ OMX Armenia SE

Emma Shand became Chairman of NASDAQ Armenia in June 2017 with the departure of Henrik Bergstrom to ADX. She is a Nasdaq Senior Advisor and member of the Borsa Istanbul-Nasdaq Strategic Partnership Committee, a Non-Executive Director of EGID Egypt and has served as a Non-Executive Member of the Kuwait Stock Exchange Transformation & Privatisation Committee upon appointment by the Kuwait Capital Market Authority.

778 Alistair Brown
CEO & Co-Founder
OpenBondX

Alistair Brown has been a pioneer in the electronic trading space, founding Lime Brokerage LLC, and previously a co-founder of Tower Research Capital, now he is trying to find his niche in the A2A bond trading business.

779 Hiroaki Okui
President & CEO
Fukuoka Stock Exchange

Hiroaki Okui, the 77 year old president & CEO of the Fukuoka Stock Exchange is making a stand to keep the regional exchange alive as Tokyo has taken almost all the flow. Given regional opportunities elsewhere there must surely be a chance for the local exchanges in the Japanese provinces. Mr Okui is endeavouring assiduously to ensure the survival of his bourse.

780 Timothy McDermott
CEO
NADEX

NADEX continues to work on being the binary exchange America likes in an era when the product line has been unfairly sullied by the actions of many rather ruthlessly short term brokers across the world.

781 Kirsten Wegner
MMI
CEO

Kirsten Wegner (a former government relations director for the International Securities Exchange) became the new CEO of the HFT lobby group Modern Markets Initiative (MMI) right on the cusp of this index closing for press. She has been with MMI since May 2016 as SVP of business development and replaces Wall Street veteran Bill Harts, who will remain with MMI as a senior adviser.

782 Krisztina Kasza
General Secretary
AFM

The arguably indefatigable Kriszti Kasza maintains a passion for her role as AFM secretary general after well over a decade in the role. Like all organisations AFM faces challenges in the short to medium term but the passion which is at the epicentre of AFM operations is distributed from an epicentre around Kriszti herself.

783 Jeff Kutler
Editor
GARP
Columnist Institutional Investor

The editor in chief of the Global Association of Risk Professionals Magazine "Ris Professional," Jeff Kutler not only writes "The Futurist" column for II he also enjoys compiling their annual Tech 40 listing.

784 Richard Berliand
Deputy Chairman
DB

Perhaps losing influence of late as the DB1 management and board have become more balkanised as a result of their own hubristic and ill-considered bid for London Stock Exchange, Berliand nonetheless has the capacity to help move DB1 forward if/when the company can release itself from the self-destructive mega-merger tailspin which has dominated the company for too many years.

785 Nadolny Taras
Chairman
Belarussian CSE

First deputy chairman of the Board of the National Bank of the Republic of Belarus Nadolny Taras is chairman of JSC Belarusian currency and stock exchange.

786 Simon Zammit
CEO
Malta SE

Having become only the third MSE CEO after Mark Guillaumier and

Eileen Muscat who stood down in late 2016, Simon is bringing a renewed focus to the business of the exchange as Malta's financial centre ambitions grows into a next stage which must surely be more reliant on capital markets than just administrative function for funds et al. He sits on the ECSDA board.

787 Benjamin North
Head of Delivery
Kynetix

Ben joined Kynetix as a Commodities SME and Head of Delivery and his primary focus is shaping how Sentinel is delivered to clients. Having both a functional and technical background, he is involved in wider initiatives such as spearheading a Blockchain Proof of Concept (POC) to writing white papers and becoming involved in consultative initiatives in the energy and agricultural markets. His vision is to help drive Kynetix's principle of digitising commodities to bridge the gap between the physical and financial markets.

788 Alban D. Chirume
CEO
Zimbabwe Stock Exchange

Prior to joining the financial sector, Alban D. Chirume was a Telecommunications Engineer at Posts and Telecommunications Corporation from 1988. In June 2009, Alban became the inaugural Chief Executive of the Securities Commission of Zimbabwe and on 1st June, 2013 was appointed Chief Executive of the Zimbabwe Stock Exchange. He is a former member of the Executive Committee Member of ASEA.

789 Elena Jakimovska Petrovska
CEO
CSD Macedonia

Elena Jakimovska Petrovska is now in her second elected term as executive director of the Macedonian CSD

790 Pall Hardarson
President
NASDAQ
Iceland

Pall Hardarson is president of the smallest NASDAQ Nordic market.

791 Richard Carleton
CEO
Canadian Securities Exchange (CSE)

Richard continues to focus on the task of building a national SME market outside the auspices of the far reaching tentacles of TMX Group and has recently enjoyed headlines championing the listing of "pot" stocks on the CSE.

792 Ahmet Yilmaz
CEO
MKK

Ahmet Yilmaz is the boss of the Turkish CSD and an ECSDA board member, having previously held senior audit positions at, amongst other markets, the Istanbul Gold Exchange and BIST.

793 Mohamed S. Abdel Salam
Chairman & MD
Misr

Mohamed S. Abdel Salam runs Egypt's CSD.

794 Fatih Savasan
Chairman
MKK

Professor Fatih Savasan was appointed chairman of the Turkish CSD in June 2017. He is vice chancellor of Milli Savunma University.

795 Gherardo Lenti Capuoduri
Head of MARKET HUB
Banca IMI

Gherardo may not be directly part of an exchange per se but his position within IMI and as boss of the MarkeHub as well as his longstanding presence around the bond market amongst other products gives him significant influence on an Italian, European and indeed, global, scale.

796 Araz Aliyev
Chairman
NDC Azerbaijan

Araz Aliyev chairs the NDC CSD in Azerbaijan.

797 Alisher Yuldashev
Chairman
Tashkent RSE

Alisher Yuldashev chairs the Tashkent Stock Exchange.

798 Mary Ann Callahan
Market Infrastructure Advisor
Paxos

Sagely advisor Mary Ann Callahan is market infrastructure advisor to Paxos, a financial technology company that is introducing Bankchain, a post-trade settlement solution for gold bullion in partnership with Euroclear, as well as other innovative securities settlement services. Previously, she was a managing director at DTCC, with more than 25 years in global relations and development in New York and London. She currently represents Paxos on two Federal Reserve payment task forces and is affiliated with Global Markets Advisory Group. Her experience also includes work as an expert advisor to the International Monetary Fund in Africa and on a World Bank expert working group.

799 James E. Newsome
NED
LedgerX

While maintaining a consultancy in Washington, former CFTC chairman and NYMEX CEO Jim Newsome is a member of the board of one of the most exciting new US ETD markets for years, the Bitcoin marketplace LedgerX which was given CFTC approval just as the EI1000 went to press.

800 Cyril Theret
CEO &
Founder IPSX

Cyril's latest venture certainly looks to be the first coherent mover amongst many business plans in the nascent property exchange sector.

801-900

801 Dorji Phuntsho
CEO
Royal Securities Exchange of Bhutan
Member of the Board SAFE

Dorji Phuntsho has been CEO of the Royal Securities Exchange of Bhutan since 2010 and previously was head of the Securities Surveillance Unit at the Royal Monetary Authority of Bhutan.

802 S. Rajendran
CEO
FT India (now 63moons)

Appointed in February 2017 when CEO Prashant Desai resigned, S. Rajendran was previously a non-executive director.

803 Allan Thomson
CEO
Dreadnought Capital

The former JSE derivatives boss has gone on to capacity building across Africa in recent years, perhaps most notably of late with the deliciously titled BADEX!

804 Adelmo J. J. Gabbi
President
Bolsa de Comercio de Buenos Aires

Adelmo J. J. Gabbi is president of the Buenos Aires BCBA stock exchange.

805 Elena Carnicero
CEO
Regis-TR S.A.

Elena Carnicero has been CEO of Regis-TR since 2014.

806 Dan Gallagher
CLO
Mylan
NED Irish SE

Dan retains influence in the parish through his board position with the Irish Stock Exchange although his latest executive position takes him some way from the SEC where as a Commissioner he was often a sole voice of coherently argued reason amongst a rather doctrinaire pro-regulation Commission post the Lehmans meltdown. A thinker whose greater presence in the parish would be very beneficial, he left Patomak advisors for Mylan earlier in 2017.

807 Peter Bennett
Founder
London Mercantile Exchange

A living legend who has been ahead of the curve for technology since, it seems, not long after Charles Babbage's message of computational engines filtered through to the masses. Peter has been a longstanding radical thinker with the likes of Tradepoint just one of many innovative ventures. Spotted Blockchain potential at the point where most folk of his generation were just getting to grips with their first mobile phone.

808 Ashraf Bin Nibhan Al Nabhani
Chairman
Muscat Securities Market

Ashraf Bin Nibhan Al Nabhani was approved as chairman of the Muscat Securities Market board in May 2017.

809 Kairat Kelimbetov
Governor
AIFC

The AIFC will incorporate AIFX, a vast new exchange which takes Astana's ambitions into a quantum leap for the financial centre, led by Kairat Kelimbetov.

810 Kofi S. Yamoah
CEO
Ghana Stock Exchange

Kofi S. Yamoah is the MD of the Ghana SE and involved in the WACMIC integration project as a board member.

811 Ghalib Mahmassani
Beirut Stock Exchange
Vice-Chairman

Ghalib Mahmassani is vice chairman of the Beirut SE.

812 George Wang
Deputy Chairman
SSX

While holding the position of deputy chairman, George Wang is the power within the Sydney Stock Exchange which seeks to build bridges between the Australian capital market and China.

813 P. Gopallen Mooroogen
Chairman
The Stock Exchange of Mauritius

814 Javier Aneiva Villegas
GM
Bolivian Stock Exchange

815 Azhari El-Tayib El-Faki
GM
Khartoum Stock Exchange

816 Michael Krume
Chairman
Munich Stock Exchange

817 Jose Gonzalo Trigo Valdivia
President
Bolivian Stock Exchange

818 John K. Kerin
CEO
Chicago SX

John K. Kerin took over as Chicago SE CEO after many years with the company when David Herron retired. As EI1000 went to press, the proposed Chinese takeover of the exchange has run into political opposition and the SEC has delayed any pertinent permissions.

819 Betsy Dorudi
Regulatory Strategy (Technology & Market Structure)
LSE

With a wealth of parish experience in addition to her day job with LSE

Group, Betsy Dorudi also represents the LSE at the European Parliamentary Financial Services Forum.

820 Sinisa Krneta
MD
Belgrade SE

821 Ian Dudden
Global Content Director, Agriculture
S&P Global Platts

One of the 'go-to' experts in commodity markets, a spell consulting successfully led to a job expanding the horizons of Platts with Australian grain futures leased to CME just one of the more notable recent successes.

822 Jonathan Seymour
Market Structure
Bloomberg

A long time LIFFE staffer Jonathan is a key figure in maintaining relations between the parish and the US information giant.

823 Mario Quarti
President of the Board
EuroTLX

824 Pascal Houangni Ambouroue
DG
Bourse des Valeurs Mobilières de l'Afrique Centrale

825 Caroline Sandura
Chairman
Zimbabwe Stock Exchange

826-850

826 Henri Claude Oyima
Chairman
Bourse des Valeurs Mobilières de l'Afrique Centrale

827 Tony Sacre
CEO
Sydney Stock Exchange

828 Linus Koh
CEO
SDiX

A co-founder of the Singapore Diamond Exchange which is the first venture seeking to build a coherent modern platform for diamonds. SDiX has reported some encouraging volume growth in its early stages as well as securing a new round of funding.

829 Chris Prior-Willeard
CEO
Hembury Associates

Longstanding market maven Chris has been especially active in post trade in recent years, building a CSD in Luxembourg but now back mostly in London.

830 Ronnie Mateo
Founder & CEO
Trumid

Mateo has had a busy year including the acquisition of Electronifie during H1 2017

831 Dra. Viviana I. Ferrari
CEO
MATBA

832 Pierre Schroeder
CEO
TradingScreen

Pierre Schroeder is the CEO of TradingScreen who stepped into the breach to fill in for Philippe Bulhannic after various unfortunate issues.

833 Hassan Manik
CEO
Maldives Stock Exchange
Member of the Board SAFE

834 Ales Ipavec
CEO
Ljubljana Stock Exchange

Ales Ipavec is bedding down the Ljubljana SE under its relatively recent new owners Zagreb SE who bought the company from Vienna Boerse.

835 Steve Smith
CEO
4th Story

Originally an IT specialist, Steve Smith was a member of the ground-breaking ePit team which was San Francisco's largest contributor to exchange technology in the original dotcom boom. Nowadays running 4th Story which delivers solutions across the range including matching engines.

836 Salim Vala
CEO
Mozambique Stock Exchange

837 Kinan Yaghi
Vice CEO
Damascus Securities Exchange

838 Marleen Evertsz
CEO
NXCHANGE

Marleen Evertsz, used to be an MD at Dutch market maker Optiver and founded NXCHANGE which seeks to shake up the process of direct capital raising and trading for stocks.

839 Antigona Bukleska Mladenovic
President of the Board
CSD Macedonia

840 Mohammad Ghassan Qalla'a
Chairman
Damascus Securities Exchange

841 Tiaan Bazuin
CEO
Namibian Stock Exchange

842 Milos Mladenovic
MD
SEEPEX

Elektromreze Srbije (EMS) has teamed up with European exchange EPEX Spot exchange, EPEX holds a 25 percent stake and EMS the remainder.

843 Bilel Sahnoun
DG
Bourse de Tunis

844 Dmitri Galinov
CEO
Fastmatch

Acquired by Euronext during Q2, Fastmatch's CEO Dmitri Galinov now has a fascinating opportunity to prove the relevance – and profitability – of his platform going forward.

845 Richard Dour
Head of International Sales
GMEX Group

Tech veteran Richard Dour is currently selling GMEX product with some notable success around the world.

846 Moremi Marwa
CEO
Dar es Salaam Stock Exchange

847 Ricardo D. Valderrama
President
Bolsa de Cereales de Buenos Aires

848 Marco Strimer
NED
LME Clear

The former Six X-clear boss has a day job as head of operations at Swiss private bank, Bank Notenstein AG and is also a NED at LME.

849 Arkady Salikov
President
BUCE Belarus

850 Ann Berg
Commodities Expert
Independent

A 'go-to' figure for agricultural commodities. No matter where or how extreme the weather, Ann Berg usually has frontline experience thereof. Former Chicago pit trader, has advised UN FAO and all manner of entities worldwide.

851-875

851 Mike Greenacre
CEO
Autilla

Runs Autilla, trying to revolutionise metals trading with NFEX, amongst other ventures.

852 Roland Tibell
Owner
Tibell & Associates

The former OMX US President now works for his own eponymous firm as well as an advisor to Bourse Consult amongst others.

853 Peter K Sitamulaho
CEO
BADEX

I still feel BADEX is missing out on a vast marketing opportunity. Will they sell me their merchandising rights?

854 Paul Bwiso
CEO
Uganda Securities Exchange

855 KH Altai
CEO
Mongolian Stock Exchange

KH Altai is pushing on improved settlement including DvP and T+3 at the Mongolian SE which continues to develop relationships with overseas bourses.

856 Alain Vandenborre
Founder & Executive Chairman
SDiX

Diamonds are a bourse's best friend? Well that's what the SDiX team clearly hope with their innovative diamond exchange bringing liquidity, risk transfer and transparency to a new asset class.

857 Ian McNaughton
Chairman
Jamaica Stock Exchange

858 David White
CEO
Riskapital Advisors

David White, amongst other tasks keeps busy undertaking assignments for WB, IFC, DFID, ADB in diverse countries (Asia, Subcontinent, Middle East, East and West Africa, Australia) relating to market regulation and market infrastructure, including demutualisation of exchanges. He has significant parish experience including with ASX and the Hong Kong regulatory body.

859 Lina Masiuliene
Director Serviced Markets
Nord Pool Spot AS (Lithuania)
APEx Member of the Board

860 Vuk Magdelinic
CEO
Overbond

861 Aco Aleksic
Chairman
Montenegro SE

862 Luca Schenk
CEO
Berne Exchange (BX)

The second Swiss Exchange is barely known but has a healthy if petite series of listings.

863 Michael Cox
Chairman
National Stock Exchange of Australia

864 Mike Sulfaro
Chief Compliance Officer
BGC Partners
WMBA Americas Member of the Board

865 Samuel Kimani
Chairman
Nairobi Stock Exchange

866 Anthony J. Saliba
NED
Chicago Stock Exchange (CHX)

The principal of Saliba Venture Management and board member of CHX has been vocal in his support for the Chinese bid for the stock exchange platform which is currently awaiting approval in the USA.

867 Ann Bowering
MD
NSX Australia

868 Asen Yagodin
Chairman
Bulgarian Stock Exchange

869 George Paresishvili
CEO
Georgian SE

870 Sunil Shah
NED
FT India (now 63moons)

Sunil Shah is MD of Motivation Engineers and Infrastructure and one of the trustees of Ankur School Trust. He retains a place on the FTIL Board which remains under significant pressure as the Indian government seeks to forcibly merge it into the failed NSEL venture.

871 Ermias Eshetu
CEO
Ethiopia Commodity Exchange (ECX)

Occupying the shoes of African exchange diva-guru Eleni Gabre-Medhin was always going to be a challenge but Ermias is pushing the ECX forward.

872 Bobby Brantley Jr.
CEO
Trop-X the Seychelles Stock Exchange

873 Dan Barnes
Editor
The Desk

One of the few journalists to make the cut. Included because he has a strong grasp on his briefs.

874 Abdutalip Sultanov
Chairman
Kyrgyz SE

875 Kosta Kostovski
President of the Board
Macedonian SE

876-900

876 Ahmad Aftab
Secretary General
SAFE Asia

877 Gilberto Pazmino Arias
President
Quito Stock Exchange

878 Marcus Killick
Chairman
Gibraltar SE

879 David Nuyoma
Chairman
Namibia SE

880 Thapelo Tsheole
CEO
Botswana Stock Exchange

881 Pervenche Beres
Member of the Econ Committee
EuroParl

"Hyperactive in the Parliament's main economic committees, and as a former ECON committee chair, she remains the go-to source for socialist ideas on economics and finance." – Politico.EU

882= Dagmar Bottenbruch /Oliver Schimek
Co Founders
Crosslend

The co-founders of this innovative bond platform earn their position of influence on the list not merely on account of their idea but also thanks to having snagged funding from CME.

883= Brian Price
Executive Chairman
FEX

"Unconventional, creative and hailed as a brilliant strategist, Brian Price is behind a deal to establish a new derivatives exchange" the Melbourne Age intoned in 2006 when hedge fund manager Brian Price first planned the opening of what was at first cumbersomely termed the Commodities and Agricultural Electronic Derivatives Exchange (Com-Agex Asia). FEX occupies the distinctive Burns Philp building dating back to 1901 at 7 Bridge Street, just across the road from the ASX HQ at number 20.

883= Dimitri Burshtein
Group Executive Corporate & Business Solutions
FEX

Dimitri has a wealth of experience from the ASX through the Australian capital market space and has been a key figure in the development of the FEX business in Sydney.

884 Ahmad Aweidah
CEO
Palestine Exchange

885 Ivan Gransky
Chairman
Bratislava Stock Exchange

886 Trevor E Blake
CEO
ECSE
ACSDA Executive Committee Member

The Eastern Caribbean SE based in St Kitts is run by Trevor Blake.

887 Vakhtang Ambokadze
General Director
ESCO
Europex General Assembly

888 Thomas Coughlin
CEO
Allocated Bullion Exchange (ABX)

ABX is one of many next generation previous metals exchanges on the market, in this case with an HQ in Singapore.

889 Fernando Yanez Gonzalez
GM
DCV

890 Sr. Marcos A. Hermansson
Chairman
MATBA

891 Christian Baer
Secretary General
Europex

892 Elizabeth Warren
Ranking Member FI & Consumer Protection Subcommittee
Senate Banking Committee

Had Hillary actually turned up and campaigned as opposed to just demanding her entitlement to the White House, by now Elizabeth Warren would have been over the horizon and way far north of here. However, with deregulation in vogue at the Trump White House, she is rather more also ran with potential to be a thorn in the side of the GOP as opposed to a genuine mover and shaker who can influence policy. However, with midterms in 2019 things could change quickly if the Democrats can get their act together.

893 Dr Rewat Bahadur Karki
Chairman
SEBON

Dr Rewat Bahadur Karki is chairman of the Securities Board of Nepal (SEBON) and was the original GM of NEPSE.

894 Lic. Rolando Duarte Schlageter
Chairman
El Salvador SE

895 Tom Glocer
Strategic Advisor
Algomi

The former Reuters CEO retains an interest in fintech and in particular serves as an advisor to Algomi. He sits on other boards including Morgan Stanley as independent lead director.

896 Nazar Niyazov
CEO
Kyrgyz SE

897 Edward Brown
CEO
GainTX SEF

898 Brian P. Lamb
CEO
Equilend Europe

899 Cecilia Ines Maya Ochoa
XM (Columbia)
APEx Member of the Board

900 Keith Davies
CEO
Bahamas International Securities Exchange (BISX)

Keith is keeping the BISX trotting along while looking at various initiatives including crowdfunding.

901-925

901 Andrew Strachan
Chairman
Bahamas International Securities Exchange

902 Andreas Schmitz
President & Chairman
Boerse Duesseldorf

903 Charles Mbire
Chairman
Lusaka Stock Exchange

904 Marco Antonio Zaldivar Garcia
President
Lima Stock Exchange

905 Betina Surballe
GM
Mendoza Stock Exchange

906 Farouq Zuaiter
Chairman
Palestine Exchange

907 Nguyen Thanh Long
Chairman
Hanoi Stock Exchange

908 Julius Akinyemi
CEO
UWIN Corp

UWIN Corp, a company founded by MIT Media Lab entrepreneur in residence and former Wells Fargo technologist Julius Akinyemi, has been given a mandate by the Cameroon government to implement a mobile-based commodity exchange.

909 Horacio Eduardo Atkinson
President
La Plata Stock Exchange

910 Jose Rafael Brenes
DG
Costa Rica SE

911 Marlon Yarde
MD
Barbados SE

912 George Bachiashvili
Chairman
Georgian SE

As chairman of both the national stock exchange and a major national investment fund, George Bachiashvili has significant clout in Georgia.

913 Roberto Abarca
GM
Bolsa de Valores de Nicaragua

914 Jorge Ernesto Perez Cuesta
President
Mendoza Stock Exchange

915 Dr Grenville Philips
Chairman
Barbados SE

916= Konstantin Saroyan
General Secretary & Member of Executive board
FEAS

An epic year for Konstantin Saroyan saw the NASDAQ Armenia bid for the HQ of FEAS succeed and he is now in office heading the organisation. I wish him every success as the organisation pivots away from its original home base of Istanbul.

916 = Hayk Yeganyan
CEO
Nasdaq OMX Armenia
FEAS Executive Board Member

NASDAQ OMX Armenia has had a complete change at the top. Chairman Henrik Bergstrom left NASDAQ for ADX and was replaced by Emma Shand while Hayk Yeganyan took over as CEO July 17 2017 with the departure of Konstantin Saroyan to head the new FEAS Secretariat relocated to Yerevan.

917 Cebotari Serghei
Chairman
Moldovan SE

918 Septimiu Stoica
President
Bursa BRM

Stoica remains the longest standing of all Romanian exchange chairmen albeit at a commodity exchange which lacks the licensing kudos of the regulated markets. He has been looking at multiple projects and given the death of SIBEX, submerged into BvB for purely political reasons, BRM may yet rise up to challenge the daft assumption that Romania can really only support a single exchange.

919 Nick Idelson
Technical Director
Tradeserve

As thinkers in the data space go, Idelson has been shaping opinions on HFT for good and bad over the years. You may not know him but you would benefit from speaking with him as he can break the complex math into simple examples and show how HFT benefits and threatens orderly markets by different degrees.

920 Laxman Neupane
Chairman
NEPSE

As we closed for press it was confirmed that Sitaram Thapaliya, the CEO of Nepal Stock Exchange Limited (NEPSE), had retired. Laxman Neupane has the job of appointing a successor who presumably will inherit the SAFE board seat of the outgoing NEPSE CEO.

921 Tarik Kurbegovic
CEO
Sarajevo Stock Exchange

Sarajevo Stock Exchange CEO Tarik Kurbegovic is a former member of the FEAS exec board as well as running the Sarajevo SE which has doubled to some 25 stocks (plus a lot of bonds and funds) since I last visited some years back.

922 Philippe Carre
Global Head of Business Development
Ullink

Philippe Carre, a GL veteran, remains a likeable figure at the heart of multiple vendor initiatives including a longstanding involvement with the likes of the FIX committee.

923 Pietro Maria Putti
Chairman & CEO
GME

Europex General Assembly

924 Bashir Mohamed Ashour
Chairman
Libyan Stock Market

925= Mike Bellaro
Plato Partnership

Plato Co-Chairman and Global Head of Equity Trading, Deutsche Asset Management.

925= Nej D'jelal
Plato Partnership

Plato Co-Chairman and MD, Head of Electronic Equities Product, EMEA, Barclays.

926-950

926 Kurt Zyla
MD
Global Head of Exchange Relationships
S&P Dow Jones Indices

927 James Ndahiro
Chairman
Rwanda Stock Exchange

928 Raul Antonio Lacayo Solorzano
President
Bolsa de Valores de Nicaragua

929 Herbie Skeete
CEO
MondoVisione

Herbie Skeete, acclaimed as a "legend in his own lunchtime" remains a popular figure in the parish having been an almost legendary figure as Reuters' point man for exchanges back in the day when the Baron's company was the world's undisputed top vendor of market data.

930 John Robson Kamanga
CEO
Malawi Stock Exchange

931 Ing. Luis Fernando Samayoa Delgado
President
National SE of Guatemala

932 Rhodri Preece-Jones
Head of European System Development
NASDAQ

A longstanding Stockholm staffer for OMX and then NASDAQ, Rhodri remains one of the more farsighted executives in the industry and retains a comprehensive knowledge of markets and issues that have arisen in and around technology during the past 20 years.

933 Konstantin Konstantinov
CEO
Independent Bulgarian Energy Exchange
Europex General Assembly

934 Badraldin Mahmoud Abass
Chairman
Khartoum Stock Exchange

935 Pierre Ekoule Mouangue
GM
Douala Stock Exchange

Douala SE is Cameroon's national market.

936 David Lawrence
COO & Company Secretary
Sydney Stock Exchange

937 Orlando Soto Enriquez
President
Costa Rica SE

938 Corneliu Dodu
President
Moldovan SE

939 Lic. Rodrigo G. Callizo
Presidente Ejecutivo
Asuncion Stock Exchange (Paraguay)

940 Tran Van Dung
Chairman
State Securities Commission of Vietnam

An interesting move taking place on July 12th, 2017 as the man parachuted in to run the Ho Chi Minh Stock Exchange from being CEO and Chairman of the Hanoi SE in March 2016. This was believed to be a prelude to a merger of the two bourses while the elevation of Tran Van Dung to being head of the regulator for Vietnam does nothing to dispel this theory. Interesting times ahead for the nascent local capital markets.

941 Simon O'Brien
Senior Manager
Market Infrastructure & Products
Abu Dhabi Global Market (ADGM)

Having oscillated between the Emirates and Australia for over a decade, Simon has been with ADGM as Senior Manager Market Infrastructure & Products since September 2015.

942 John Serocold
Principal
Studio Serocold

John Serocold, who was previously a senior director at the International Capital Markets Association and before that played a leading role in the LIBA heyday, remains on the radar of many organisations working behind the scenes.

943 Nilca Hurtado
DG
Bolsa Nacional de Productos Panama

944 Marcelo Often
GM
Montevideo Stock Exchange

945 Mark Grave
CEO
Australian Wool Exchange

One of the world's more obscure bourses, the Australian Wool Exchange continues to find a niche for a product which remains at once ubiquitous but yet strangely lacking homogeneity as, contrary to intuition, sheep are in fact all different.

946 Michal Cabala
Chairman
OKTE
Europex General Assembly

947 Peter Toth
CEO
HUPX Europex General Assembly

948 Michelle Persad
CEO
Trinidad and Tobago Stock Exchange

949= Cameron & Tyler Winklevoss
Joint CEOs
Gemini / Winklevoss Bitcoin Trust

The Winkelvoss twins have suffered various setbacks and are currently in regulatory limbo with their BTC ETF plans which must be a bitter pill to swallow as the cryptocurrency has exploded in value.

However they have regained some impetus as this index closed for press with news of their deal to licence their Gemini cryptocurrency exchange data to CBOE.

950 Esat Bilici
General Secretary
Konya Commodity Exchange

Konya Exchange is located in the Central Anatolia region of the country, in the seventh most populous city in Turkey.

951-975

951 Anila Fureraj
GM
Tirana Stock Exchange

952 Augustine Chithenga
Chairman
Malawi Stock Exchange

953 Pablo Sitjar Pizzorno
President
Montevideo Stock Exchange

954 Mrs Zaheera Baba-Ari
CEO
Nigeria Commodity Exchange (NCX)

955 Tebogo C. Masire
Chairman
Botswana Stock Exchange

956 Neil Grover
CEO
COMDAQ Metals

Amidst the myriad hype of new electronic platforms for metals, it would be easier to overlook COMDAQ Metals which has been a competitor platform to the incumbent exchanges for nearly 20 years. MIFID II is a challenge but Neil Grover remains good humoured about the fascinating days ahead for metals trading. Moreover COMDAQ Metals own a fascinating portfolio of IOSCO compliant indices in a variety of very esoteric precious metals.

957 Peter Goenczi
CEO
Aktietorget

This Swedish alternative market is nowadays powered by the Nordic Growth Market trading system and is one of many ventures from Scandinavia and the Baltic states seeking to reorient SME funding.

958 Stein Ole Larsen
CEO
NOREXECO

NOREXECO is the pulp and paper exchange based in Norway.

959 Amar Kuchinad
CEO
Electronifie

Electronifie was acquired by trumid earlier in 2017.

960 Ray A. Sumairsingh
Chairman
Trinidad and Tobago Stock Exchange

961 Kaarel Ots
Chairman
NASDAQ Estonia

962 Alexander Belozertsev
President
Alexandra Inc

A living legend from Moscow who has been closely involved in many parish projects – last seen in the Middle East developing grain silos and warehouses.

963 Boris Abramovic
CEO
HROTE
Europex General Assembly

964 Jurgen Wahl
Member of the Executive Board
EXAA
Europex General Assembly

965 Gabriel Purice
CEO
BRM

966 Michael Philippou
President & CEO
LAGIE
Europex General Assembly

967 Hermann Hamlet
EVP
Bolsa de Valores de la Republica Dominicana

968= Le Hai Tra
Chairman
Ho Chi Minh Stock Exchange

968= Nguyen Vu Quang Trung
CEO
Ho Chi Minh Stock Exchange

It is unclear how long Le Hai Tra or Nguyen Vu Quang Trung will last in position (appointed mid August 2017) not because of their own abilities but because a Hanoi – Ho Chi Minh merger appears to be on the cards fairly soon. Previous chairman Tran Van Dung who has run both Hanoi & Ho Chi Minh bourses became chairman of the State Securities Commission on July 12th 2017.

969 Anze Predovnik
GM
BSP Regional Energy Exchange, Slovenia

970 Oleg Tkachenko
CEO
Ukrainian SE

971 Etienne Nel
CEO
ZarX

Creating the first new stock exchange licence in ZA in 100 years has proven a daunting task as JSE offered remarkable pushback but now, with the licence in hand, it will be interesting to see just how much progress 4AX can make given the tricky economic background in the Republic of South Africa.

972 Lou Severine
CEO
NYIAX

Lou Severine is on a mission to bring advertising to the exchange industry, or rather a coherent exchange to the advertising industry.

973 Fariyal Mukaddam
CEO
4AX

974 Nguyen Thi Hoang Lan
Acting CEO
Hanoi Stock Exchange

All positions appear somewhat temporary for now in the Vietnamese capital markets as the likelihood is of a merger in the short term is high between the incumbent markets in Hanoi and Hochiminh.

That said Hanoi received the mandate to open derivatives trading and did so under the watchful gaze of many national dignitaries as well as the Chairman and CEO on August 10th as this book went to press.

975 Jose Rizek Guerrero
President
Bolsa de Valores de la Republica Dominicana

976-1000

976 Vasil Simov
Chairman & CEO
Sofia Commodity Exchange

977 Valia Theodoraki
CEO
Cayman Islands SE

978 Joyce Dlamini
GM
Swaziland Stock Exchange

979 George Dallas
Policy Director
International Corporate Governance Network (ICGN)

Dallas is a vocal exponent for corporate governance and has been voluble of late about the issues arising from Brexit through to the possible listing of Saudi Aramco shares which involves bending existing listing norms.

980 Jose Arturo Alvarado
President
Central American Bourse (Honduras)

981 Georg Aasen
Head Nasdaq Oslo & VP Nasdaq Commodities
Europex General Assembly

982 U Yin Zaw Myo
MD
Yangon SE

So far the Daiwa Institute of Research, backed Yangon SE may have only 4 listing but a new corporation law is passing through the administration which will allow for foreign market access.

983 Victor Ionescu
CEO
OPCOM
Europex General Assembly

Boss of the OPCOM exchange which is backed by the Romanian government.

984 Vincent Ivosa
Acting GM
Port Moresby Stock Exchange

985 Jitesh Surendran
CEO
Mercantile Exchange Nepal
Member of the Board SAFE

986 Edward Katimbo Mugwanya
Chairman
Alt-X

Alt-X is a nascent new Ugandan exchange.

987 Vijay Satyal
CEO
Everest Commodity Exchange

988 Nur Bano Ali
Chairman
South Pacific Stock Exchange

989 Alisher Shernazarov
CEO
CASE (Tajikistan)

CASE is being rolled out in Tajikistan in partnership with GMEX.

990 Rodney Doyle
Director of Market Operations & GM
SEMO
Europex General Assembly

991 Manuel Joaquim De Lima
President
Bolsa de Valores de Cabo Verde

992= Brian Liston
President & Director
992= Edward Woodford Exec Dir
Seed Commodities Exchange (Seed CX)

Founders of Seed CX, a venture, like Americanex, with designs on the cannabis related marketplace.

993 Bola Onadele Koko

CEO
FMDQ OTC Securities Exchange

994 Craig Fuller
CEO
TransVix

Craig Fuller aims to create the first national US trucking futures market.

995= Nicolas Berggruen
Partner

995= Tony Elumelu
Partner & Chairman of the Board
AFEX

EAX East Africa Exchange is amongst the subsidiaries of this organisation seeking to create markets in Africa.

996 Krishika Narayan
Acting CEO
South Pacific Stock Exchange

997 Nagaev Aziz Ravilevich
Acting Executive Chairman
Uzbek Commodity Exchange

998 Hong Sok Hour
CEO
Cambodia Securities Exchange (CSX)

999 Vankham Voravong
CEO
Lao Securities Exchange

1000 Tracey Roberts
Communications & Policy Adviser
FESE

Tracey Roberts has much of the European stock trading universe in her Rolodex and without her deft touch, FESE conferences and other events, let alone lobbying coordination, would be much less efficient.

Relegations

Alas a few folks made it through the 2016 list but when it came to the first published list for 2016/2017 they were squeezed out, mostly thanks to the demise of the CME Europe operations simply reducing their overall Influence rating – at least for now. Hopefully they can bounce back next year.

The relegations in no particular order are:

Michael Lewis
Author: "Flash Boys"

Michael Lewis was a wildly important figure in the parish thanks to penning the Flash Boys book but a year or two on and his overall presence has reverted to merely world famous pithy business author...

Simon Raybould
NED
CME Europe (closed)

Simon Raybould slipped out of the rankings when CME Europe closed.

Mark Spanbroek
Chairman CME Europe (closed)
NED Aquis Exchange

Mark Spanbroek remains a NED at Aquis Exchange but by dint of CME Europe closing down where he was Chairman, he slipped out of the top 1000 ranking

Dr. Hans-Bernd Menzel
NED
CME Europe (closed)

Dr. Hans-Bernd Menzel slipped out of the rankings when CME Europe closed.

Bill Harts
Senior Advisor (former CEO)
MMI

With former ISE Government relations director Kirsten Wegner stepping up from her position as SVP of business development to take the CEO position at the HFT lobby group Modern Markets Initiative (MMI) in August 2017, she squeezed industry veteran Bill Harts out of the list at the 11th hour.

Mack Gill
former CEO
Millenium

Mack Gill may have made it yet again into the 2017 Institutional Investor Tech 40 but in reality he was already heading to the exits as London SE reorganised its IT arrangements (again).

Charlotte Crosswell
former CEO
NLX

Charlotte Croswell departed NLX and then the venue was eventually put out of its misery a few months later. Just as we closed for press she re-emerged with a post as interim CEO of a UK quango Innovate Finance during the search for a replacement for departing CEO Laurence Wintermeyer. While holding a portfolio of NEDs such as a DL consortium Cobalt and an fx broker Freemarket, it was unfortunately not sufficient to keep Charlotte in the EI1000 most influential list.

Resignations

The following all departed their parish positions and thus lost their influence. Some have left the industry, many are gardening and thus likely to return while others have set up on their own in some shape or form and indeed also may make a return in the near future to the EI1000 Index.

Brendan Bradley
Head of Innovation
EUREX

Brendan Bradley, perhaps one of the finest product developers in the entire history of the ETD parish left DB1 in what seems a bygone era – that early period when the parish had confidence in Carsten Kengeter. Brendan is now dabbling in fintech.

Tim Thurman
CIO
ASX

Popular Canadian CTO decided the heat and sun of Sydney was no match for those long winter's nights and cool white climes of Canadian winter.

Alan Gandelman
CEO
ATS Brazil

The boss of the upstart market ATS Brazil is now running Intl FC Stone in Brazil.

John Fildes
CEO
Chi-X Australia

John Fildes exited stage left from Chi-X claiming a clash of cultures while the new owners of Chi-X have inferred a rather robust criticism of his management style. Either way his departure leaves him out of the ranking for now.

Danny Corrigan
CEO
CME TR

The popular Danny Corrigan may have departed CME but he had a storming year. A leading contra-EU thinker (one of the few represented at the senior level of the City UK), Danny departed the CME TR he had set up and was last seen in the windy steppes advising the Astana International Financial Centre.

Cees Vermaas
CEO
CME Europe

Cees Vermaas rather controversially dropped Euronext at the IPO stage for the new CME Europe Exchange and, alas, the move to London did not ultimately go well. It would be difficult to pin much blame at Cees' door all the same as CME seemed to often blow hot and cold about its European exchange. Moreover nobody seemed inclined (or perhaps it was incentivised) to take risks. Thus volumes were sluggish and eventually the CME Europe dream was killed by Terry Duffy soon after assuming supreme commander powers within CME Group.

Maria Joao Borges Carioca Rodrigues
CEO
Euronext Lisbon

Maria resigned after being asked by the Government of Portugal to join the Management Board of Caixa Geral de Depósitos. I was sorry to see Maria go as she was making a sound fist of running the Euronext Lisbon operation, establishing a new IT subsidiary to help the organisation move forward but a juicy banking post was just too attractive...

Jos Dijsselhof
COO
Euronext

Jos Dijsselhof stepped down as Euronext Amsterdam CEO on June 30th 2017.

Mustafa Baltaci
Secretary General
FEAS

Mustafa Baltaci stepped down as Secretary General of FEAS when the secretariat moved to Yerevan, Armenia. Now specialising in Turkish fintech having previously been a leading figure in the Istanul Exchange scene, Mustafa remains a decent member of the parish who was on the wrong end of the politics of BIST.

Prashant Desai
CEO
FTIL/63 Moons

In the fog of the NSEL scandal, management upheaval at FTIL has been considerable.

Garry Jones
CEO
LME

Garry Jones found himself on the wrong end of just one too many problems at LME at a volatile time and paid the price. Doubtless likely to bounce back once the garden has been sufficiently spruced up.

Stuart Sloan
COO
LME

Stuart is expected to return to the parish soon...

Paul Smyth
CEO
Kynetix

Paul Smyth, a cofounder and CEO of Kynetix is now Chairman of the company but as a pure non executive he has sliped out of the 1000 index.

Anabela Chambuca
CEO
Mozambique Stock Exchange

Anabela Chambuca stood down as Mozambique SE boss in October 2016 and stepped up to the fascinating challenge of heading the office of the First Lady of Mozambique.

Chitra Ramkrishna
CEO
NSE India

A somewhat cloak and dagger departure. Chitra Ramkrishna disappeared abruptly at the end of 2016 and has barely been heard of since. Rumours abound but the facts dictate that a highly capable exchange executive has alas left the parish.

Subramanian Anand
Group COO
NSE India

Subramanian Anand was a somewhat controversial figure during the Chitra Ramkrishna NSE era who left when she came under fire on various fronts, including his hiring.

Olivier Gueris
COO
Qatar Stock Exchange

I expect we will see the former Qatar COO Olivier Gueris return to the parish in the near future but for now he is gardening and planning his next move.

Christian Katz
CEO
SIX Swiss Exchange

Christian Katz left SIX and the FESE Presidency mid-term. Now with a fascinating portfolio of financial / fintech entities building up he is some way ahead of those at SiX who stayed longer but have been purged under the Lacher Chairmanship...

Urs Ruegsegger
Group CEO
SIX
acting Chairman WFE

Still in office at the time of writing but could be gone by the time we print, hence firmly in the resignations column and outside the 1000 for now. Was it the curse of the WFE, a voluntary decision or a manouevre by activist chairman Romeo Lacher? In any case Urs Rüegsegger is standing down as the boss of SiX just when he had become Acting Chairman of WFE, that currently posioned chalice of career ends, after

Chitra Ramkrishna resigned almost as swiftly as she first assumed the Chairmanship only months earlier.

Willem Meijer
CEO
TOM MTF

The founder of TOM Willem Meijier stepped down as CEO in 2016 having co founded the platform. Within a few months the fascinatingly dynamic market that couldn't quite turn a profit was being shut down...

Hans Pieterse
CEO
TOM MTF

Having stepped into the CEO role, the strategic assessment rapidly moved to be one in favour of closing the TOM venue.

Osman Sarac
CEO
BIST

Another departed head of BIST we barely had time to get acquainted with.

Per Sjoberg
CEO
TriOptima

Per Sjoberg founded TriOptima. Everybody who has ever hedged or swapped anything ought to be forever in his debt. He stood down from NEX earlier in 2017 and I wish him every success wherever life takes him.

Gil Mandelzis
CEO
EBS BrokerTec

Gil Mandelzis stepped back from tunning EBS Brokertec what seems an age ago but it was in the twinkling of the creation of NEX. Again likely to bounce back soon.

Robbie McDonnell
MD Sales
APAC Trading Technologies

The perenially popular Irishman who had sold TT all over the world stood down from the company but will remain based in Asia. I wish Robbie McDonnell all the very best - if nothing else he has been one of the finest third party endorsers of "Capital Market Revolution!" for the past 18 years!

Evgeny Fetisov
CFO
MOEX

Evgeny Fetisov left the parish to become CFO of Luxoft

Pawel Tamborski
CEO
Warsaw Stock Exchange

Pawel Tamborski was certainly of the calibre to lead the GPW (unlike some who have come after him) but the direct swap from government to government gerrymandered exchange management was, frankly, sleazy. He did a reasonable job but in the end his party was boooted out by the voters for being useless and the de facto new communists were elected who set about purging anybody not sufficiently ideologically pure to their belief system. Now caught in a possible fraud trial which looks frankly a bit of a political fix up even without getting into the details. Hopefully better days await him.

Malgorzata Zaleska
CEO
Warsaw Stock Exchange

There have been GPW bosses who rarely left Warsaw – Ludwik Sobolewski in his heyday was one but Malgorzata Zaleska was in a whole different league. It was broadly impossible to tell if she was in the building and certainly there was never any evidence of her being in charge of anything during her mercifully brief tenure as CEO of a stock exchange where she demonstrated a litany of reasons why academics ought not to be parachuted in to run market infrastructure.

Rafal Antczak
CEO
Warsaw Stock Exchange

Rafał Antczak had one of the shortest tenures in parish history as a CEO. No sooner had yet another GPW EGM elected him than it appears he may have been thought to be doctrinally impure by the de facto new communist governent of Poland. He never truly assumed office and stood down.

Pawel Dziekoński
Deputy CEO
Warsaw Stock Exchange

GPW VP Paweł Dziekoński was just another of the casualties of the ongoing government cleansing programme in the ranks of the management of the Warsaw Stock Exchange.

Ireneusz Lazor
CEO
PolPX/TGE

Ultimately he was the man who made PolPX hugely successful but that didn't count for much when the government changed. Ireneusz Lazor may return to the EI1000 in due course but for now he is the former CEO of the Polish Power Exchange.

Elmer Funke Kupper
CEO
ASX

Elmer Funke Kupper was the man who defined passive aggressive parish tactics. Unfortunately something to do with suitcases and dictators came back to challenge him from his days in the betting industry. Unlucky but at the same time, while some are so sleazy to hang on despite the accusations, at least common sense prevailed in the departure of Elmer Funk Kupper. His lasting legacy is debatable as he was a brooding presence propagating a monopoly at the expense of a market structure but at least he left wthout too much prodding when his number was up.

Lord Jonathan Hill
Commissioner
DG Markt

Lord Hill probably never expected to be mentioned in this parish bible of influence but until June 23rd 2016 he was a vital link: the man charged with the task of running financial service regulation for the EU. Subsequently, he has reinvented himself and came out as a true patriot and forward thinker, building the Prosperity UK conference with hedge fund manager Paul Marshall to shape the future of Britain post Brexit. We will doubtless hear more of Lord Hill albeit he may not revert to the top 100 of the parish influence list again.

David Lester
Chief Strategy Officer
LSEG

David Lester may yet return but for now the LSE Group veteran has left Paternoster Square where he was most recently Chief Strategy Officer.

Muhammad Zafar-Ul-Haq Hijazi
former Chairman
SEC Pakistan
former IOSCO Member of the Board

Chairman of the SEC Pakistan who oversaw his national bourses fused into a single entity, then IPO'd after a Chinese consortium bought a cornerstone stake. More recently the Pakistani SEC chairman was under some legal duress concerning possible falsification of records charges and was threatened with arrest during July, leading to his stepping down as Chairman of the SECP.

Retirements

Note in some cases, 'retirement' is purely from the position which garners influence in the parish directly e.g. as Chairman of an exchange or industry body but the person may still be actively working in an executive career.

Marwan Al-Bataineh
Chairman
Amman Stock Exchange

Marwan Al-Bataineh left as his term was over at the start of 2017.

Dr Yusuf Mansur
Chairman
Amman Stock Exchange

Dr Yusuf Mansur became chairman of Amman SE in early 2017. His career has spanned various sectors including telecoms and a spell at the UNDP. He was (for reasons which are not clear as this came right as we closed for press) replaced in August as Chairman of the government controlled Amman SE by Dr. Jawad Anani (himself appointed as a government representative on the board as of 26th July 2017).

Edemir Pinto
CEO
B3

The man who all but unified Brazil's entire market structure, Edemir Pinto stood down as CEO soon after the creation of B3 when Cetip was folded into BM&F Bovespa.

Jeremy Penn
CEO
Baltic Exchange

Worked at Reuters for years. Went on to run the Baltic. Sold it to SGX. Pocketed bonus. Retired.

Khaled Zribi
Chairman
Bourse de Tunis

Term over.

Anthony Browne
CEO
British Bankers Association

With the British Bankers Ascoaition being folded into a new super industry body across 5 areas, Anthony Browne stood down as the last CEO of the British Bankers Association.

Timothy G. Massad
Chairman
CFTC

Sometime – it all seems so long ago – there was media without Donald Trump being accused of colluding with Russia and Tim Massad was Chairman of the CFTC.

Phupinder Gill
CEO
CME Group

It goes without saying that when I back tested our data, in previous years Gill would have been as high as number one in this index! By far the biggest departure in 2017, Gill's retirement as CEO of CME not only robbed the parish of one of its most popular and charismatic figures it also reduced the cumulative mileage of the entire exchange CEO cadre materially! Much missed. Good luck to Gill as he spends more time with multiple generations of family.

William J. Brodsky
Chairman
CBOE

Bill Brodsky's long farewell was so considerable it almost surprised parishiooners when suddenly he was no longer there!

Fascinatingly, within a year his CBOE has been transformed through the BATS deal.

Edward L. Provost
President & COO
CBOE

CBOE COO Edward L. Provost retired and moved to consulting after the conclusion of the BATS acquisition.

Susan Phillips
NED
CBOE

Retired from the board on the takeover of BATS but the former CFTC Commissioner and Professor emeritus at George Washington University remains active in other entities.

Feng Bo
CEO
Dalian Commodity Exchange

Dalian Commodity Exchange CEO Feng Bo retired having overseen the market become a metals powerhouse.

Marton Nagy
Chairman
Budapest Stock Exchange

Marton Nagy retired as Chairman of the Budapest SE.

Lars Hille
Chairman
Frankfurt Stock Exchange

Term over

Tim Howell
CEO
Euroclear

Tim Howell retired as Euroclear CEO. After a spot of gardening may yet return to the list in non-executive form...

John J "Jack" Brennan
Chairman
FINRA

Term ended in June 2017 for the former Vanguard funds boss.

Sarah O. Alade, Oon
Chairman
FMDQ OTC Securities Exchange

The Chairman of the Nigerian OTC market reached the end of her term.

David Strongin
GFMA
Executive Director

David retired early in 2017 from his post with GFMA.

Megain Widjaja
CEO
ICDX

Megain Widjaja retired as CEO of ICDX to be replaced by the brilliant Lamon Rutten.

Paul Swann
President
ICE Clear Europe

I am not even sure Paul has left the building yet per se but his trailed retirement was so clear we moved him into the Retirement column ahead of his departure despite it being clear ICE would like him to stay. Off to spend more time at his stately pile in the country ("Swannston Abbey"), I wish Paul every success and happiness in what could be a very long retirement indeed.

Sir Robert Reid
Chairman
ICE Futures Europe & ICE Clear Europe

After an epic 18 years as ICE Futures Europe Chairman, Sir Robert retired to acclamation for his strong role in overseeing what was a key element in the growth of ICE.

Mike Gibson
COO
ICE Clear Europe

Mike began a mini reshuffle of ICE Clear senior management in 2016.

Ayyaz Afzal
CEO
Islamabad Stock Exchange

Retired on the merger of Islamabad SE into a unitary Pakistan Stock Exchange.

Hamad Abdullmohsen Al-Marzoq
Chairman
Kuwait Stock Exchange

Term over.

Eileen Muscat
CEO
Malta Stock Exchange

Eileen Muscat may have left the parish directly after her lengthy tenure as CEO of the Malta Stock Exchange but she has been a fabulously successful figure in the backhround during the EU's recent Maltese presidency where she herself presided over various working fora in the clearing and settlement field. Who knows where her next moves lie...

Eddy Njoroge
Chairman
Nigeria Stock Exchange

Retired after 9 years on the board, for 6 of which he was Chairman

Tim Bennett
CEO
NZX Limited

Tim retired after his 5 year term expired in May 2017.

U.K. Sinha
Chairman
SEBI

U.K. Sinha retired as SEBI Chairman to be replaced by Ajay Tyagi.

Mary Jo White
Chairman
SEC

Mary Jo White stood down as SEC Chairman with the new Republican administration in office.

Ann Small
GC
SEC

Left in January 2017 as the Trump Presidency began.

Satyananda Mishra
Chairman
MCX India

Term over.

Stephen Lansdown
Deputy Chairman
The International Stock Exchange (TISE)

The high profile British financier stepped down in June 2016 as the Channel Islands SE adopted its much more ambitious name!

Chew Choon Seng
Chairman
SGX

The former CEO of Singapore Airlines stepped down in September 2016.

Song Anping
Chairman
Shanghai Futures Exchange

Gui Minjie
Chairman
Shanghai Stock Exchange

Song Liping
President & CEO
Shenzhen Stock Exchange

Song Liping stood down as (the first female) Shenzhen Stock Exchange President & CEO in October 2016 to be replaced by Wang Jianjun.

Richard Swift
CEO
Yieldbroker

Retired after 15 years running the Australian swaps platform.

Gary Katz
CEO
ISE

Gary Katz for me defined the modest greatness of the best exchange executives. A brilliant brain, a broad streak of modesty and a politeness that prevailed at all times. He saw the opportunity with David Krell to revolutionise the options market when essentially nobody else did and he deserves all the rewards that he reaped from his innovative excellence.

Alexandre Zeller
Chairman
SIX

Alexandre Zeller stepped down as Chairman of SIX late in 2016. Since then Romeo Lacher has somewhat changed things...

Muhammad Badul Mazid
Chairman
Chittagong SE

Left office just before the excitement began of seeking a cornerstone shareholder for 25% of the exchange ahead of an IPO.

N.Rangachary
Chairman
CDSL

N.Rangachary, who chaired the board of CDSL since 2010, retired in May 2016 at the end of his term.

S Ramadorai
Chairman
BSE India

Retired in March 2016 after serving 6 years.

Sudhakar Rao
Chairman
BSE India

Retired at the end of June 2017 having first led the BSE to a successful IPO.

S.B Mathur
Chairman
NSE India

Retired 2016 before various clouds engulfed the NSE.

Sitaram Thapaliya
CEO
NEPSE
Member of the SAFE Board

Retired from his position in July 2017.

Nadeem Naqvi
CEO
PSX

Nadeem Naqvi left office as the first CEO of the unified Pakistan exchanges once he had completed his term in mid 2017.

RIP

In a parish that is thousands of years old, the ravages of time affects us all and sadly this section lauds some of those from amongst our number who have met their demise. In keeping with the longer creation period of the 2017 index, the following is a selection of deceased parishioners over the past couple of years.

As a footnote I have tended to append just one parish title to each deceased party but in reality they did a great deal more than just a single exchange function. Some, for instance Clayton Yeutter, went on much higher office still.

Jean-Francois Theodore
former CEO
Euronext

Jean-Francois was a unique figure in the parish and its development. He truly revolutionised many aspects. Quiet and softly spoken he was nonetheless prone to many pithy remarks: "just because you are old doesn't make you a benchmark" (referring to an antiquated clearing system) was just one which springs to mind. ParisBourse looked to be stuck before he lead the deal which created Euronext and subsequently placed Euronext under the wing of NYSE.

It wasn't just these deals which were notable. Throughout his career when he looked to be up against it Jean-Francois found a way out – he bought a significant stake in the nascent GL Trade when their front end ate the incumbent ParisBourse system's market share. Meanwhile his deal pushing LIFFE into play was a masterstroke – winning the day when the London Stock Exchange provided the copybook how not to do a deal pitch against Jean-Francois' genius.

Jean-Francois was a great man and always interesting company.

Rory Collins
former CTO
ASX

I'm typing with tears in my eyes as I recall all the great parishioners who passed on during the long genesis of this project. None saddened me more than that wonderful character Rory Richmond Collins, an english gentleman who took Australia to his heart and the antipodes reciprocated by loving him back. The man who was CTO when ASX became the first major exchange to go electronic from floor trading. A process deftly described by Rory as "a bit like changing all 4 engines simultaneously on a Boeing 747 "jumbo jet." In mid air."

A unique character whose funeral was packed to the gills in Sydney – frankly had his sons livestreamed the wake it would have made one of the biggest parish IT events in years.

When you're feeling down: recall one of Rory's elegant remarks, made via telephone to the sounds of a glass being brought from the cupboard and delicately wiped with a cloth, the fridge opening and shutting, much shuffling in the drawer and then the sound of corkscrewing giving way to the delicate pouring noise in the background. At this point Rory interjected to my side of the conversation by saying "You know, there are only 5 words which can rescue this day from being a drag, Cape Mentelle Semillon Sauvignon Blanc. Cheers!"

Hans Tietmeyer
former President
Bundesbank

RIP a key architect of the Euro who became rather ambivalent about the single currency in his twilight.

Clayton Yeutter
former President
CME

A CME President and Chairman, an Agriculture secretary under Ronald Reagan, Clayton Yeutter lived the life of a commodity legend who was often seen on either side of the Atlantic and the Pacific. RIP.

Alan Whiting
former Chairman
LIFFE

During a varied bureaucratic career, Alan worked for the UK Civil Service in various influential positions, for instance serving as a member of IOSCO Technical Committee and representing the UK in G7 tasks pertaining to financial regulation, as well as a multitude of other committee posts while he was a a leading figure in the executive creating the UK Financial Services Authority.

I came to know Alan best when he joined LME as executive Director of Regulation and Compliance (from 1997). Alan was appointed to the LIFFE board in 2006 and rose to become Chairman in 2012 while he was also Chairman of the Gibraltar Financial Services Commission. Amongst other boards, he was a non-executive director of NYMEX London.

Alan died in mid 2015 after a recurrence of cancer.

Chris Keith
former CTO
NYSE

Chris Keith, like Rory Collins, came from an entirely different era of exchange IT but they both developed their thinking to stay consistently ahead of the curve long after their primary CTO careers had ended. Another unique character (when will we have a celebratory concert of some of his opera I wonder?) Chris was an inspiration in the development of markets who I first met in the early stages of what ultimately became Intrade / Tradesports during a time when the first of many (unrealised) Open Exchange concepts were in circulation.

Tom Healy
former CEO
Irish Stock Exchange & Abu Dhabi Stock Exchange

It's difficult to really believe Tom Healy has passed away. The man who oversaw the revolution in the Irish Stock Exchange and subsequently ran the Abu Dhabi Exchange was simply so much larger than life it is all but impossible to believe we have been robbed of his genial presence. A good man, he was in many ways the saviour of the Irish nation's capital market. Ultimately Tom did much more for his country and the parish than either ever recognised while always being highly amusing and delightfully politically incorrect.

Raj Bagri
former Chairman
LME

Raj Bagri was the Chairman of LME who oversaw much modernisation even by the sleepy standards of that traditional organisation. His passing was mourned from the UK to India and throughout the world of metals trading.

Paul-Andre Jacot
former Chairman & CEO
SFOA

RIP the man who was often the life and soul of SCFOA / SFOA and who worked tirelessly to make it what it was. A longstanding chairman, then longstanding CEO and ultimately the man at the epicentre of the rise and subsequent decline of what was once the best conference in derivatives, Burgenstock.

Duff Scott
former Chairman
TSX

RIP The chairman of the TSX from 1987-1989, Duff Scott was honoured to hold the position his father had also occupied some decades earlier.

Gary Anderson
former CEO
DGCX

Gary suffered terminal cancer in November 2014, slightly ahead of the EI1000 calculation period but I see no point in being a stickler for rules. Like all good parishioners, he deserves a moment for our reflection on his many achievements, particularly in energising the DGCX.

John Pearce Bunting
former President & CEO
TSX

John Pearce Bunting a former TSX CEO and President passed away in 2017. He was the longest office holder as leader of the exchange serving 17 years from 1977 to 1994. He was a true visionary and marketplace innovator, leading Toronto Stock Exchange to defining achievements including becoming the first exchange in the world to offer fully-automated trading with the launch of the Computer Assisted Trading System, or CATS, in 1977. He also presided over the development of the world's first ETF in 1990 (Toronto 35 Index Participation Fund) and was President of the FIBV (forerunner of the WFE) from 1983-1984.

Ivers Riley
former CEO
HKFE

RIP Ivers Riley. It's difficult to know quite how to pitch things about great men and this was a figure who deserves huge plaudits for his gentle style, his excellent foresight and the vision he brought to all manner of projects from single stock futures as CEO of Hong Kong Futures Exchange through to his work chairing the launch of ISE. RIP a great man who materially improved the parish before his death at the age of 82 in early 2015.

As a C-suite executive with a genuine comprehension of the innovative process, Riley stood out in many areas. He was a leader in the creation of the ETF movement, as one of the parents of the SPDR ETF based on the S&P 500 Index while Senior EVP of derivatives at AMEX (he also worked previously at CBOE and NYSE). In that sense, Riley galvanised the ETF movement, perhaps the ultimate example of a "people's derivative."

He had 2 spells as CEO of the HKFE from 1994-1997 and again 1999-2000. He was also influential as Chairman of the revolutionary options market the International Securities Exchange where he worked with co founders Gary Katz and David Krell to deliver a remarkable new vision of options trading which genuinely pivoted the whole industry into a new space, not merely electronic but with considerable institutional presence too. As Chairman Ivers led the IPO – the second in north America by an exchange following in the footsteps of CME. A non-executive director of ISE from ISE's foundation in 2000 until 2007, Ivers subsequently, served as a non-executive director of Interactive Brokers (2008-2014).

Unstintingly polite, Riley was one of the few executives in the exchange space at the time who could see many ways in which markets would change going forward during the 1990s when a certain blinkered complacency had overwhelmed many in the industry.

Ronald Li
former Chairman
Hong Kong Stock Exchange

Ronald Li, the somewhat infamous Chairman of the Hong Kong Stock Exchange died on December 27th 2014 and was buried on January 8th 2015.

Li founded the Far East Stock Exchange in 1969 and in 1986 became the head of the HKSE after the merger of the four HK stock markets (the others being Kam Ngan SE and Kowloon SE). However perhaps his most famous moment came in 1987 when, faced with a massive panic, Li closed the HKSE for 4 days, reopening on October 26th one week after "Black Monday." The market promptly lost one third of its value.

Despite LI expressing a "clear conscience" that he had made this move in the best interests of the exchange and not any personal conflict of interest. Li was nonetheless to end his career in disgrace after he was convicted of accepting bribes in relation to exchange listings.

Li worked in the Stanley Prison library during his prison sentence for 9 HK dollar per day although given he had a portfolio estimated to be worth 10 billion HK dollar (1.3 billion USD), rumours abounded that he earned around HK$5 million per day during his incarceration of 30 months from a 4 year sentence. He was reputedly worth US$2 billion by the time of his death.

Amongst his very well connected and successful family, Li's brother Simon Li Fook-Sean (who predeceased him in 2013 aged 91) was the first Chinese judge to become Chief Justice of the SAR after the Hong Kong handover from the British to China.

I never met Ronald Li but the wonderful raconteur and former ASX CTO Rory Collins (sadly also a member of this RIP section) was at his best when recalling a meeting with Li at the height of his powers as the first unified HKSE Chairman only months before the crash of 1987.

Despatched from Sydney to see if other exchanges might be interested in the new Australian system then being rolled out, Rory was courteously welcomed by Ronald Li. Nevertheless, the HKSE Chairman appeared slightly sceptical about the whole notion of the digital bourse (after all HKEX struggled to end fixed commission stock dealing until relatively recently).

When Li enquired what exactly was the point of this new-fangled electronic means of dealing, Rory Collins enthusiastically suggested wondrous market friendly concepts like "Liquidity, Accessibility and Transparency!"

Li pondered for a split second and then responded:

"Well we certainly don't want any of that around here."

Neil de Sena
Managing Partner
SenaHill Partners

Neil de Sena met a premature demise in February 2017. He was a true fintech pioneer who is perhaps best remembered not just for his eponymous fintech merchant bank SenaHill Partners but being the creator of the early ECN RediBook.

Harold Marvin Williams
former Chairman
SEC

Harold Marvin Williams served as chairman of the SEC between 1977 and 1981 after a successful career in industry and academia. He subsequently became the first President and CEO of the J Paul Getty Trust which he ran with brio and success for many years, retiring in 1998 on his 70th birthday.

Magnus Bocker
Former President
NASDAQ

Fortunately this section ends here. Tragically it ends with the demise of a highly popular figure in the parish who was, like Neil de Sena amongst others, taken from this world far far too prematurely. Magnus Bocker was a colourful character who tragically died after a battle with cancer, just as the EI 1000 went to press.

Indeed Magnus still qualified for the 1000 list until his demise thanks to his position as Chairman of a fintech fund and also as Chairman of the Singaporean shareholders association. I know from my mailbox and conversations around the parish that Magnus is already much missed.

Yossi Beinart
former CEO
TASE

Stop press. Alas I spoke too soon. Yossi was somewhat hounded from office as TASE CEO while suffering health problems which ultimately proved overwhelming in late August 2017.

Yossi had returned to his native Israel to run the Tel Aviv Stock Exchange but he had made his mark on the parish for some years, most notably as CEO of NADEX in the US.

While it had appeared sadly inevitable we would be writing his obituary sooner or later, the event came soon enough that I stopped the presses and had time to insert this modest tribute to another great man amongst the many who left our parish this year. All of them made an amazing impact while they were with us and are already greatly missed. RIP one and all.

Sub Lists

The Sub Lists

Selecting from the EI1000 data leads to some interesting sub divisions of the overall list.

Exchange CEOs

As the exchange is at the backbone of why you're reading this tome, I thought it would be fun to look at the 25 most influential exchange CEOs:

1 Jeffrey Sprecher ICE

2 Charles Li Xiaojia HKEX

3 Adena T. Friedman NASDAQ

4 Edward T. Tilly CBOE

5 Thomas Farley NYSE

6 Terrence A. Duffy CME Group

7 Xavier Rolet KBE LSEG

8 Brad Katsuyama IEX

9 Akira Kiyota Japan Exchange Group

10 Carsten Kengeter DB1

11 Gilson Finkelsztain B3

12 Jos Schmitt Aequitas

13 Alexander Afanasiev Moscow Exchange

14 Deirdre Somers Irish Stock Exchange

15 Matt Chamberlain LME

16 Ashishkumar Chauhan BSE

17 Vikram Limaye NSE India

18 Nicky Newton-King JSE

19 Liu Nengyuan Shanghai Futures Exchange

20 Richard Sandor American Financial Exchange

21 Hu Zheng China Financial Futures Exchange

22 Wang Jianjun Shenzhen Stock Exchange

23 Mrugank M. Paranjape MCX

24 Stephane Boujnah Euronext

25 Shozo Ohta Tokyo Financial Exchange

Exchange Chairmen

NB This list excludes those exchange chairmen who are also CEO...

1 Donald Brydon CBE LSEG

2 Wu Qing Shanghai SE & CEINEX

3 Chow Chung Kong HKEX

4 Joachim Faber DB1

5 Li Zhengqiang Dalian Commodity Exchange

6 Rick Holliday-Smith ASX

7 Alexey Kudrin Moscow Exchange

8 Aime Ruiz Sacristan BMV (Mexico)

9 Len-Yu Liu Taifex

10 Jun-Ji Shih Taiwan SE

For those who are curious, the following 4 occupy dual positions and would have made this list had they not been excluded for also being CEO:

1 Jeffrey Sprecher ICE Chairman & CEO Chairman of NYSE

2 Craig S. Donohue OCC Exec Chairman & CEO

3 Terrence A. Duffy CME Group Exec Chairman & President

4 Richard Sandor Chairman & CEO American Financial Exchange

CCPs

A difficult category this as various parties have other responsibilities. Expect some tweaking to the 2018 model.

1 Craig S. Donohue OCC Exec Chairman & CEO

2 Kimberly S. Taylor CME Group

3 Adrian Farnham LME Clear Ltd CEO

4 Thomas Hammond ICE Clear US President

5 Calvin Tai Chi Kin HKEX Joint COO

6 John McPartland Federal Reserve Bank of Chicago Senior Policy Advisor Financial Markets

7 Suneel Bakhshi LSEG CEO LCH Group

8 Gaurang Desai DGCX CEO

9 Conny Anderson NASDAQ

10 John P. Davidson OCC COO

IDBs

1 Michael Spencer ICAP Group CEO

2 Howard W. Lutnick BGC Chairman and CEO

3 Lee Olesky Tradeweb CEO

4 John Phizackerley Tullet Prebon CEO

5 Patrick Combes Tradition Chairman & CEO

6 David Casterton TP ICAP Vice Chairman

7 Colin Heffron GFI Group CEO

8 Godfried De Vidts NEX Director of European Affairs

9 Ken Pigaga NEX Global COO

10 Daniel Marcus CEO ParFX

Regulators

1 Margrethe Vestager DG Comp EU

2 Steven Maijoor ESMA Chairman

3 Jay Clayton SEC Chairman

4 J. Christopher Giancarlo CFTC Chairman

5 Shiyu Liu China Securities Regulatory Commission Chairman

6 Andrew Bailey Financial Conduct Authority UK CEO

7 Ajay Tyagi SEBI Chairman

8 Gerard Rameix Autorite des Marches Financiers (AMF) President

9 Ashley Ian Alder Securities and Futures Commission Hong Kong CEO

10 Ryozo Himino Financial Services Agency Japan, Vice Minister for International Affairs

Politicians

1 Steven Mnuchin US Government Treasury Secretary

2 Donald Trump US Government POTUS

3 Pier Carlo Padoan Government of Italy Minister of Finance

4 Orrin Hatch US Senate Chairman Senate Finance Committee

5 Bill Huizenga US House of Representatives Chairman of subcommittee on capital markets securities and investments

6 Mitch McConnell US Senate House Majority Leader and member of the Senate Agricultural Committee

7 Michel Barnier EC EU Chief Negotiator on Brexit

8 Jeb Hensarling US House of Representatives Chairman House Financial Services Committee

9 K Michael Conaway US House of Representatives Chairman House Agricultural Committee

10 Pat Roberts US Senate Chairman Senate Agricultural Committee

Central Bankers

To commemorate quantitative easing, I have actually added a dozen to this list of the most influential central bankers in the parish. It seemed appropriate:

1 Janet Yellen US Federal Reserve Board Chairman

2 John McPartland Federal Reserve Bank of Chicago Senior Policy Advisor Financial Markets

3 Mario Draghi ECB President

4 Jens Weidmann Bundesbank President

5 Benoit Coure ECB Member of the executive board

6 Yves Mersch ECB Member of the executive board

7 Andrew Hauser Bank of England Director for Banking, Payments, and Financial Resilience

8 Mark Carney Bank of England Governor

9 Martin Moloney Central Bank of Ireland, Ireland Head of Markets Policy Division

10 Nadolny Taras Belarussian CSE Chairman

11 Sabine Lautenschlager ECB Member of the executive board

12 Jaime Caruana BIS GM

Dealmakers

1 Jeffrey Sprecher ICE Chairman & CEO

It has not been a frantic year or two. Recently a few modest incremental deals have been closed but nothing passes through the parish without it being shown to Jeff Sprecher.

2 Michael Spencer ICAP Group CEO

Investments in fintech galore now need to show some progress from the various ventures in NEX Optimisation and Euclid ventures in particular as Michael himself builds a whole new NEX from the hiving off of the voice broking bulk of ICAP.

3 Charles Li Xiaojia HKEX CEO

Delivering a series of links to China has been the latest string of dealmaking for Charles Li.

4 Howard W. Lutnick BGC Chairman & CEO

Next step a new Brokertec killer which also eats the lunch of NASDAQ's eSpeed? It's on the agenda...

5 Edward T. Tilly CBOE CEO

Surprised the parish by buying BATS and launching CBOE towards the top of tier two markets in Young's exchange pyramid. Will there be more?

6 Lance Uggla IHS Markit President

Lance Uggla avoided the threat of an ICE predator and presuming he takes the top position as expected, he has a remarkable balance sheet at IHS Markit to propel himself forward.

7 Chris Concannon CBOE President & COO

Deftly dealt his business into CBOE and now has the chance to modernise the group's technology.

8 Lee Hodgkinson Euronext Head of Markets & Global Sales of Euronext; CEO of Euronext London

Lee was omnipresent as Euronext suddenly began to do deals: Algomi, EuroCCP, Fastmatch et al; a failed tilt at Clearnet but a deft dalliance with ICE softened up LCH. Euronext is pushing into new areas and demonstrating it has no intention of being caught up in the lazy fallacy that it was just a tasty morsel ready to be acquired by a predator.

9 Peter Reitz European Energy Exchange

The man who can do deals at DB1 through his fascinating and dynamic EEX enterprise.

10 Jon Moulton The International Stock Exchange Chairman

Yet to do any deals on the exchange front, apart from opening a rep office in the Isle of Man but as one of the biggest names in UK PE it would be impossible to close out this top 10 without mentioning the chairman of the Channel Islands Stock Exchange.

Visionaries

The people who aren't looking from one day to the next but are way beyond that into the next domain, perhaps another dimension: those are the visionaries. They think things or do things that are just not spotted by the crowd.

This list also fascinates me because some of those with less influence overall may have a greater visionary status but like all the lists, I have left them in the order in which the main Index of Influence places each person. Moreover data here are taken not just for the past year but over a longer swathe as it can sometimes be difficult to perceive vision when looking at a narrow time window!

Also it's slightly longer than average with 20 names but at least it is heartening to think we can muster at least 20 visionaries in the parish (and there are more)...

1 Jeffrey Sprecher ICE Chairman & CEO

One of my closest associates praises Jeff Sprecher and the ICE team by saying "these people made fools of the incumbents" or words to that effect (AKA he doesn't actually say "incumbents" per se). Jeff Sprecher is looking at the chessboard with the seasoned expertise of a grand-master. He has a clear execution focus on victory while many others are just hoping to stay a turn ahead of the frey, at best. The ICE team do a brilliant job day to day executing the plan while Jeff considers the field of play holistically. Moreover the broad parish now believes in Jeff's vision – the ultimate recognition of a visionary leader.

2 Michael Spencer NEX Group CEO

Who knew that one moneybroker working in Tokyo could go on to take on the world? Michael spotted the opportunities and made ICAP the number one from nothing and now he has taken the digital assets to move NEX forward.

3 Lance Uggla IHS Markit President

Even today try pitching the idea of IHS and half the parish (at best) would think you bonkers. That's vision and Lance Uggla has shown a consistent ability to find remarkable niches to profit from where nobody else was looking or computing.

4 Thomas Peterffy Chairman Interactive Brokers LLC

Building the biggest network of market makers of the early electronic age was one thing, taking that network and using it to power perhaps the greatest brokerage of the current age – now that's visionary.

5 Brad Katsuyama IEX Cofounder & CEO

If you haven't read Flash Boys, I see no point in explaining further. Michael Lewis wrote the book of Brad. I add him to the list without any intention of poorly paraphrasing Lewis' excellent tome.

6 Jos Schmitt Aequitas President & CEO

Amongst the greatest folks you can meet are those who abandon consultancy to follow their dream. Jos led a monster entity in Capco but he still headed to Canada, built a network which threatened TMX so they bought him out. Then (and BTW somebody somewhere ought to have been shot for this omission), he walked out of TMX and after a pause is doing it all over again. True TMX haven't bought him out yet but then again as a company struggling for vision....

7 Nils-Robert Persson Cinnober Chairman

Nils-Robert understood the linkage between technology and markets inherently from participating in the rise of OMX. He took that kernel of an idea out to build a better exchange system and is now championing real time clearing in a way no other vendor has yet been able to replicate. The fact that Brazil's CETIP alone was able to announce savings of over 6 billion dollars in collateral for clients of the unified B3 powered by the Cinnober system speaks volumes as to Nils-Robert's vision in exchange and CCP technology.

8 Richard Sandor Chairman & CEO American Financial Exchange

It's remarkable to consider that Richard invented financial futures for the modern world then went on to invent environmental finance and now as an encore, is reworking bank financing for smaller financial institutions. That is merely a skim of the career metadata of Professor Richard Sandor who is simply a genius when it comes to market structure foresight.

9 Luc Bertrand Vice Chairman, National Bank Financial Group

Years ago they agreed to divorce the cash equity market and the derivatives markets in Canada. The Toronto exchange could not believe that the foolish "Frenchies" wanted the off balance sheet marketplace. So the TSX paid them alimony for the cash market listings. Before the non-compete expired a decade later, Luc Bertrand who had seen the vast opportunity more clearly than anybody, was rewarded handsomely along with his shareholders by the TSX whose top tier vision rarely seems to stretch much beyond the scope of Bay Street and their lakeside summer cottages.

10 David Weild Weild & Co

David is the Father of the JOBS act who brought modern equity crowd-funding to life against essentially all odds.

11 David Hardy Chairman GCSA

Nowadays the LCH reaps the rewards of having been the first to offer CCP services in OTC financial markets. Yet at the time it was David Hardy as LCH CEO who had to push to make Repoclear, Swapclear et al a reality against an incumbent oligopoly and governmental/regulatory indifference. So, when the EU wants to blame somebody for the success of Euro clearing in London, ironically the major culprit is David Hardy who championed OTC CCP when nobody else was interested, least of all in Europe.

12 Eleni Gabre-Madhin Eleni CEO

Eleni saw the opportunity to build exchanges in Africa starting with her native Ethiopia and is doing so with aplomb having been CEO of ECX and now leading her eponymous exchange building company.

13 Michael Aitken CMCRC

The Prime Minister of Australia reckons Michael is a pretty brilliant bloke and so does Exchange Invest! His SMARTS surveillance system was sold to NASDAQ while his CMCRC team remain at the forefront of global market research from their Australian base.

14 Peter Jessup NASDAQ

Peter Jessup is a tech guru who solves the problems of the future: a brilliantly clear mind filtered through an expansive memory. He's a Kiwi chip off the old block in the same way that Bruce McLaren was one of the greatest engineering minds in motorsport history.

15 Craig Heimark DB1 Supervisory Board

Fabulously clear thinker from the original O'Connor partner ranks with a brilliant vision for the future.

16 Scott Gordon RCG Chairman & CEO

Way back when the CME was on the verge of civil war, Scott Gordon was the compromise candidate who climbed onto the bridge of CME as Chairman and set about changing every vestige of that business, setting out the precepts that have enabled it to become the electronic powerhouse it is today.

17 Richard Olsen Lykke

Richard was ahead of the forex game with OANDA and its fabulous platform. Now he is doing things in Distributed Ledgers while others are still threatening a PoC.

18 James E. Oliff former Deputy Chairman, ex-NED CME Group, CME Europe, CME Clearing Europe

Jim Oliff did so much to bring his beloved CME forward that it is still difficult to believe that era is over. His vision remains acutely clear and the pace of change of markets make it all the more useful in these exciting times. My own vision suggests CME may rue the day they let Jim walk from the board after his sterling service and many initiatives when chairing the Strategic Planning and Electronic Transition Committees which at the turn of this century put much of the meat onto the bones of the desire for CME to become a modern market. Whatever the case with CME, the Oliff vision remains entirely intact and hopefully will be deployed coherently in more markets soon.

19 Patrick L Young DV Advisors Exec Director

Way back when books were never to be seen outside of paper, the parish seemed rather surprised by the way I saw things going. Well that proved a lot more correct than frankly I ever anticipated. Skimming through the metadata, over a decade later I realised there was a need for a proper 'parish' newsletter. Even my own beta testers all thought it was a terrible idea. So here I am editing and publishing the first listing of the most influential 1000 people in the market structure arena which my selfsame beta testers aren't so keen on. Now for my next trick...

20 David Cummings Tradebot Chairman

Dave Cummings invented the concept of BATS and did so from the sort of city New Yorkers only consider when they watch road movies. Dave saw the future and moved with alacrity to create the Better Automated Trading System. The rest is history at least on that story, as Cummings' retains an eye for a good many fascinating projects...

Thinkers

Here are a dozen folks who when you're stuck on the linear plane you need to consider as a healthy source of alternative thought. Their precise computative power is not necessarily ordered here as they are listed according to their ranking in the overall index of influence:

1 Lee Olesky Tradeweb CEO

2 Shiyu Liu China Securities Regulatory Commission, Chairman

3 David Goone ICE CSO

4 Charles Vice ICE President and COO

5 Chris Concannon CBOE President and COO

6 Paul Atkins Patomak CEO

7 John McPartland Federal Reserve Bank of Chicago Senior Policy Advisor Financial Markets

8 Gedon Herschten Hertshten Group Founder & Chairman

9 Seth Merrin Liquidnet CEO

10 Mike Aikins Chi-X Oz CTO

11 Mark Beddis BIDS Strategic Advisor

12 Jake Pugh Independent

Ten To Watch

I have taken the liberty of omitting the obvious names in the top ten. Of course watching whatever Jeff Sprecher does is a vital precept of parish life. Likewise, the ways in which Michael Spencer and Howard Lutnick respond to challenges will be massively interesting.

Rather I have chosen here some names outside the top 10 who have been flagged up by the algorithms as having particularly interesting prospects to make a difference in the next year through their particular strands of influence. Watch these figures make great strides forward in the next year.

1 Hans-Ole Jochumsen NASDAQ President, Global Trading & Market Services

Back in Europe with a great linkage to the US, now is the time Hans-Ole can reshape the strategic side of the NASDAQ European operations. He is the ideal man in the ideal place and this is an ideal time for NASDAQ to evolve further as a cohesively strategic entity.

2 Lynn Martin ICE Data Services President and COO

Big data, Lynn sits on more of it than most and thus her opportunity is everywhere, how she exploits it will be fascinating to watch and indeed pivotal to underpinning ICE's earnings.

3 Ajay Tyagi SEBI Chairman

Is Tyagi really going to make progress or will the socialist regression of India's regulatory blob hold him prisoner?

4 Matt Chamberlain LME CEO

Matt is already steering a course towards detente with the brokers and that will be a key facet in rejuvenating the LME going forward under his watch.

5 Vikram Limaye NSE India CEO

NSE has had its first genuine crisis (actually crises to be precise, they just all came at once). As the first "outsider" to head the largest Indian exchange, he ought to provide a fascinating insight into Indian markets and how they cope with the future.

6 Christoph Boschan CEESEG Member of the Management Board of Wiener Borse, CEESEG Management

Having been brought in to rejuvenate the ailing Vienna exchange, Christoph has approached the task with relish. It's a long way to exit the forest yet but at least there is momentum building.

7 Gaurang Desai DGCX CEO

With DGCX now making vast progress on multiple fronts, amongst the most exciting developments for Gaurang Desai and his team in the next 12 months will likely emerge from the MOU signed with ADX in July 2017 about developing a unified clearing house for the UAE.

8 Peter Reitz EEX CEO

Peter Reitz is perhaps the only senior manager in DB1 to have had a good year – and indeed his past year was absolutely marvellous. Can he be the internal pick to lead the group if Carsten is forced out? Whether or not he achieves a promotion, the realpolitik is that his EEX empire within the DB1 group is the only business unit which looks fighting fit and progressive right now.

9 Lamon Rutten ICDX CEO

Former UNCTAD commodities guru and MCX boss Lamon Rutten has been in Indonesia running the ICDX for some months, expect to see the results begin to take hold during the next year.

10 Richard Olsen Lykke

Olsen is in the blockchain field and has a fascinating model, actually doing business...a lot more progressive than the proof of concept merchants. Always at the cutting edge of innovation and poised for a fascinating DL future.

Women (World)

This list focuses on the leading women in the parish at global level and is then broken down in subsequent lists by region.

1 Adena T. Friedman NASDAQ President, COO

2 Kelly Loeffler ICE SVP, Corporate Communications & Marketing

3 Lynn Martin ICE Data Services President and COO

4 Kathleen M. Cronin CME Group Senior MD, GC

5 Deirdre Somers Irish Stock Exchange CEO FESE President

6 Kimberly S. Taylor CME Group President, Global Operations, Technology & Risk

7 Verena Ross ESMA Executive Director

8 Janet Yellen US Federal Reserve Board Chairman

9 Nicky Newton-King JSE CEO

10 Sharon Y. Bowen CFTC Commissioner

Women USA

1 Adena T. Friedman NASDAQ President, COO

2 Kelly Loeffler ICE SVP, Corporate Communications & Marketing

3 Lynn Martin ICE Data Services President and COO

4 Kathleen M. Cronin CME Group Senior MD, GC

5 Kimberly S. Taylor CME Group President, Global Operations, Technology & Risk

6 Janet Yellen US Federal Reserve Board Chairman

7 Sharon Y. Bowen CFTC Commissioner

8 Kara M. Stein SEC Commissioner

9 Brenda Hoffman NASDAQ CTO

10 Blythe Masters Digital Asset CEO

Women UK

1 Caroline Silver Moelis MD

2 Diana Chan EuroCCP CEO

3 Tina Hasenpusch CME Clearing Europe CEO

4 Ruth Crowell LBMA

5 Kirstina Combe London Metal Exchange Head of Regulatory Strategy and Government Affairs

6 Fiona Le Poidevin Channel Islands SE (now TISE) CEO

7 Angela Knight Senior Independent NED, Tullet Prebon

8 Jenny Knott NEX Optimisation CEO

9 Niki Beattie Market Structure Partners CEO

10 Kay Swinburne MEP

Women Europe ex-UK

1 Deirdre Somers Irish Stock Exchange CEO FESE President

2 Verena Ross ESMA Executive Director

3 Elisabeth Roegele BaFin

4 Anna Kuznetsova Moscow Exchange MD of Securities Market, Member of the Exec Board

5 Sabine Lautenschlager ECB Member of the executive board

6 Anneli Tuominen ESMA / FIN_FSA Vice-Chairman / DG

7 Veronica Augustsson Cinnober CEO

8 Iwona Sroka KDPW CEO ECSDA Executive Committee member

9 Hauke Stars DB AG Member responsible for Cash Market, Pre-IPO & Growth Financing

10 Heike Eckert Eurex Clearing AG Deputy CEO

Women Middle East Africa & Asia

NB I have used slightly different methodologies for women compared to the overall geography lists where there is an amalgamated "Europe" and a CEESEE list.

1 Nicky Newton-King JSE CEO

2 Yupawan Sirichainarumitr The Stock Exchange of Thailand MD

3 Eleni Gabre-Madhin Eleni CEO

4 Sarah Al-Suhaimi Tadawul Chairman

5 Nonkululeko Nyembezi-Heita Johannesburg Stock Exchange Chairman

6 Rinjai Chakornpipat The Stock Exchange of Thailand Senior Exec Vice President

7 Kesara Manchusree The Stock Exchange of Thailand President

8 Zeona Jacobs Johannesburg Stock Exchange (JSE) Director Marketing and Corporate Affairs

9 Leanne Parsons JSE Director Trading and Market Services

10 Ashima Goyal MSEI Chairman

Established Entrepreneurs

They are now heading established leading enterprises in their fields but they began as startups in some shape or another. IMHO, this list is one of the most important in the entire 1000 index complex as it reflects those who stepped out to create businesses where others either couldn't discern an opportunity, or couldn't make it work.

1 Jeffrey Sprecher ICE Chairman and CEO

2 Michael Spencer ICAP Group CEO

3 Lance Uggla IHS Markit President

4 Thomas Peterffy Interactive Brokers Chairman

5 Michael Bloomberg Bloomberg CEO

6 Nils-Robert Persson Cinnober Chairman

7 Ken Griffin Citadel CEO

8 Gedon Herschten Hertshten Group Founder & Chairman

9 Seth Merrin Liquidnet CEO and Founder

10 Patrick M. Byrne Overstock CEO and founder

StartUp Entrepreneurs

It's impossible to say how many of this list will survive, let alone who will thrive but each in their own way is working on fascinating projects to create value in new projects.

1 Brad Katsuyama IEX Cofounder & CEO

2 Ronan Ryan IEX President & Co Founder

3 Neal Brady Eris Futures CEO

4 David Weild Weild & Co

5 Christian Martin TeraExchange CEO & Cofounder

6 Alasdair Haynes Aquis Exchange CEO

7 Hirander Misra GMEX CEO & Cofounder

8 Morgan Downey Money.net CEO

9 Kaidi Ruusalepp Funderbeam CEO & founder

10 Patrick L Young DV Advisors Exec Director

Industry Associations

A dozen of the most prominent folk in the industry associations – a mix of Chairmen and the diligent executives of the associations themselves:

1 Scott O'Malia ISDA CEO

2 Martin Scheck ICMA CEO

3 Deirdre Somers Irish Stock Exchange CEO FESE President

4 Paul P. Andrews IOSCO Secretary General

5 Walter Lukken FIA President & CEO

6 Michael Dawley Goldman Sachs & Co. FIA Chairman

7 Rainer Riess FESE DG

8 George Handjinicolaou ISDA Deputy CEO and Head of EMEA

9 Rene Karsenti ICMA President

10 Robin Martin World Gold Council

11 Simon Turek CME Senior Director Govt Relations EACHCCP.eu Chairman

12 Rafael Plata EACHCCP.eu SG

Tech Gurus

Markets are tech in so many respects, it was a challenge to choose just the 20 folks who stand out on the tech front as having a certain guru star power. Here are the top 20 identified as being tech gurus from the EI1000. True some might occupy senior management jobs nowadays but all of them are more than capable of getting their digits dirty in a bit of code if necessary:

1 Thomas Peterffy Chairman Interactive Brokers

2 Brad Peterson NASDAQ Chief Information Officer

3 Harris Brumfield Trading Technologies Chairman

4 Lars Ottersgard NASDAQ EVP Market Technology

5 Veronica Augustsson Cinnober CEO

6 Chris Corrado LSEG Group COO, Group CIO

7 Peter Jessup NASDAQ EVP

8 Mayur Kapani ICE CTO

9 Jim Bird BIDS Trading President & CTO of BIDS Trading Technologies

10 Rob Park IEX Group CTO

11 Richard Leung HKEx

12 Nick Themelis MarketAxess CIO

13 Brian Taylor BTA CEO

14 Mike Aikins Chi-X Oz CTO

15 Bob Caisley NASDAQ

16 Eric Scott Hunsader Founder Nanex

17 Paul Pickup Trading Technology

18 Jim Northey Itiviti Consultant

19 Peter Bennett London Mercantile Exchange Founder

20 Rhodri Preece-Jones NASDAQ Head of European System Development

FinTech

The issue with this list was discerning who is actually in fintech and who is just fin trying to use tech to make them look glamourous – a tricky difference to discern and in the end the list of the 20 key folks in fintech (not Blockchain) looks like this:

1 Neal Brady Eris Futures CEO

Far and away the most successful of the new independent swap platforms but then again Neal Brady has a holistic understanding of the business he is in and the means to deliver the solutions.

2 Christian Martin TeraExchange CEO and Co-Founder

Likewise TeraExchange has been highly rated for its technology development.

3 Rumi Morales CME Ventures CEO

As boss of the CME venture fund which is aimed at really finding the "new new" thing to aid multi billion dollar CME expand, Rumi has considerable fintech influence.

4 Morgan Downey Money.net CEO

Can Morgan Downey be the (Irish)man who finally has developed a device to take on the incumbent vendors?

5 Patrick L Young DV Advisors Exec Director

Having written the original book on fintech "Capital Market Revolution!" a handy decade before anybody used that word, bear in mind I was already a 5 year veteran of online e-commerce when that was published in 1999. I have been fairly busy since too on the fintech front...

6 Andrew Hauser Bank of England Director for Banking, Payments, and Financial Resilience

A man within the Bank of England who has shown considerable prescience of thought in his approach to fintech – which raises him head and shoulders above most central bankers, let alone the core banking cousins who compare unfavourably with the intergenerationally inbred...

7 David Gurle Symphony CEO & Founder

The messaging app that got a shot in the arm from Bloomberg's privacy shenanigans, still making inroads into the marketplace.

8 Sunil Hirani trueEX Co-founder & CEO Member of the Board, co-founder DAH

A sound tech understanding powers not just TruEx but also drove Sunil Hirani's understanding of the blockchain to make him a co founder of Digital Asset Holdings.

9 Anil Stocker MarketInvoice CEO

MarketInvoice is the invoice platform which has really done amazing things from the UK.

10 Stu Taylor Algomi CEO

Futuristic vendor trying to rework the bond market amongst others with backing from Euronext.

11 Phil Bird Perfect Channel CEO

The guru of auctions, Phil Bird's Perfect Channel is the benchmark for any kind of auction process in any marketplace imaginable.

12 Jeff Lynn Seedrs CEO

One of the greats of the first phase of equity crowdfunding, building a successful business from the UK.

13 Matt Dolton Kynetix CEO

Warehousing commodities and similar processes are at the core of the Kynetix product base – vital stuff in an era where commodity settlement is more important than ever.

14 Anthony Tassone GreenKey Founder & Chief Product Officer

Nifty products and solutions for age old problems including that archaic but still with us concept of the trading turret – now with new GreenKey features to make it more reliable and safer than ever.

15 Linus Koh SDiX CEO

The Singapore Diamond Exchange is also testing Blockchain technology as part of its operation to develop the exchange marketplace in diamonds.

16 Steve Smith 4th Story CEO

Steve runs 4th Story, a US west coast vendor with clients globally which has provided all manner of solutions and is now in the business of providing matching engines too.

17 Mike Greenacre Autilla CEO

Metal aforethought for Autilla as they progress with their platform launch for NFEX, the Martin Abbot exchange startup.

18 Dagmar Bottenbruch /Oliver Schimek Crosslend co-ceo / founder and co-chief executive

A tech oriented bond platform backed by CME Ventures.

19 Julius Akinyemi UWIN Corp CEO

Man on a mission to build a mobile-based commodity exchange for Africa.

20 Lou Severine NYIAX CEO

Powered by NASDAQ, Lou Severine is leading a bid to make a market in advertising.

Blockchain

Everybody is talking about it but few seem to know about it. Here are 15 people who have a clear understanding of the new DL Blockchain world of cryptocurrency and by the way, the list is in accordance with overall influence ranking per se. So the total Blockchain knowledge is not necessarily correlated with the rankings here qv Ron Bernstein and the Winkelvoss twins in particular!

1 Peter Randall SETL CEO

2 Blythe Masters Digital Asset CEO Member of the Board

3 Fredrik Voss NASDAQ blockchain guru

4 Steve Gibson NEX CEO, Euclid Opportunities

5 David Rutter R3 CEO

6 Richard Olsen Lykke

7 Matt Trudeau Tradewind Markets (& IEX) President

8 Patrick M. Byrne Overstock CEO and founder

9 Kaidi Ruusalepp Funderbeam CEO and founder

10 Patrick L Young DV Advisors Exec Director

11 Eddie Astanin National Securities Depository of Russia

12 Sunil Hirani trueEX Co-founder & CEO Member of the Board, co-founder DAH

13 Paul Chou LedgerX CEO, Co-Founder

14 Ron Bernstein Augment Partners

15 Cameron and Tyler Winklevoss Winklevoss Bitcoin Trust / Gemini CEO

North America

Let's kick off the list of major players region by region in the parish's strongest region, North America. Note this list reflects where participants are based as opposed to where they may have influence from a different continent or region:

1. Jeffrey Sprecher, Chairman & CEO, InterContinental Exchange
2. Howard W. Lutnick, Chairman & CEO, BGC
3. Adena T. Friedman, CEO, NASDAQ
4. Craig S. Donohue, Executive Chairman & CEO, OCC
5. Edward T. Tilly, CEO, CBOE
6. Thomas Farley, President, NYSE Group
7. Thomas Peterffy, Chairman, Interactive Brokers LLC
8. Jay Clayton, Chairman, SEC
9. Terrence A. Duffy, Exec Chairman & President, CME Group
10. J. Christopher Giancarlo, Chairman, CFTC
11. Lee Olesky, CEO, Tradeweb
12. Steven Mnuchin, Treasury Secretary, US Government

Europe

I have not made a specific UK versus EU list, rather this list is Europe all the way to central Europe with a subsequent CEESEE list all the way to Russia:

1. Michael Spencer, CEO, NEX Group
2. Margrethe Vestager, Commissioner, DG Comp EU
3. Donald Brydon CBE, Group Chairman, LSEG
4. Lance Uggla, President, IHS Markit
5. Steven Maijoor, Chairman, ESMA
6. Xavier Rolet KBE, CEO, LSEG
7. Carsten Kengeter, CEO, DB
8. John Phizackerley, CEO, TP ICAP
9. Hans-Ole Jochumsen, President Global Trading & Market Services, NASDAQ
10. David Peniket, President, ICE Futures Europe
11. Andrew Bailey, CEO, Financial Conduct Authority UK, IOSCO Member of the Board
12. Joachim Faber, Chairman, DB

S-E Asia

This list is South East Asian without Mainland China:

1 Charles Li Xiaojia, CEO, HKEX

2 Akira Kiyota, CEO, Japan Exchange Group

3 Chow Chung Kong, Chairman, HKEX

4 Ashley Ian Alder, CEO, SFC Hong Kong, IOSCO Chairman

5 Ryozo Himino, Vice Minister for International Affairs, FSA Japan

6 Trevor Spanner, Group CIO, HKEX

7= Roger Lee, Joint COO, HKEX
7= Calvin Tai Chi Kin, Joint COO, HKEX

9 Shozo Ohta, President & CEO, Tokyo Financial Exchange

10 Wen-Chang "Peter" Chiu, CEO, Taiwan Futures Exchange Corporation

China

Mainland China:

1. Shiyu Liu, Chairman, China Securities Regulatory Commission, IOSCO Member of the Board
2. Wu Qing, Chairman, Shanghai SE, Chairman of CEINEX
3. Li Zhengqiang, Chairman, Dalian Commodity Exchange
4. Liu Nengyuan, President & CEO, Shanghai Futures Exchange (SHFE)
5. Hu Zheng, CEO, China Financial Futures Exchange, CEINEX Board Member
6. Wang Jianjun, President & CEO, Shenzhen Stock Exchange
7. Zhang Shenfeng, Chairman, China Financial Futures Exchange, CEINEX Supervisory Board
8. Huang Hongyuan, President, Shanghai Stock Exchange, CEINEX Supervisory Board
9. Wu Lijun, Chairman, Shenzhen Stock Exchange
10. Chen Huaping, Chairman, Zhengzhou Commodity Exchange

Subcontinental Superstars

How does the parish looks in the Indian subcontinent? Well this year 100% Indian:

1. Ajay Tyagi, Chairman, SEBI
2. Ashishkumar Chauhan, CEO, BSE India
3. Vikram Limaye, CEO, NSE India
4. Mrugank M. Paranjape, CEO, MCX India
5. J Ravichandran, Group President, NSE India
6. Ashok Chawla, Chairman, NSE India
7. Samir Shah, CEO, NCDEX
8. Rabi Narayan Das, Chairman, NCDEX
9. Saurabh Chandra, Chairman, MCX India
10. Dhirendra Swarup, Chairman, BSE India

Middle East

1. Essa Abdulfattah Kazim, Governor, DIFC, Chairman DFM & Bourse Dubai NED NASDAQ
2. Ahmed Bin Sulayem, Chairman, DGCX
3. Rashid bin Ali Al-Mansoori, CEO, Qatar Stock Exchange,
4. Gaurang Desai, CEO, DGCX
5. Mohammed Al-Jadaan, Chairman, CMA
6. H.E. Sheik Ahmed Bin Jassim Bin Mohammed Al-Thani, Minister of Economy & Commerce Chairman, Qatar Stock Exchange
7. Khalid Abdullah Al Hussan, CEO, Tadawul
8. Sarah Al-Suhaimi, Chairman, Tadawul
9. Hamad Abdulla Al Shamsi, Chairman, Abu Dhabi Securities Exchange
10. Hassan Abdulrahman Al Serkal, COO, Dubai Financial Market

CEESEG

From the Oder river east to Moscow (and theoretically beyond) this list mixes the New Europe with Vienna amongst other cities...

1. Alexander Afanasiev, CEO, Moscow Exchange
2. Alexey Kudrin, Chairman, Moscow Exchange
3. Anna Kuznetsova, MD Securities Market, Moscow Exchange
4. Christoph Boschan, CEO, CEESEG
5. Petr Koblic, CFO, CEESEG, FESE Member of the Board
6. Iwona Sroka, CEO, KDPW, ECSDA Executive Committee member
7. Sergei Poliakoff, CIO, Moscow Exchange
8. Alexey Rybnikov, President, St. Petersburg International Mercantile Exchange
9. Ludwik Sobolewski, CEO, Bucharest Stock Exchange
10. Ivana Gazic, CEO, Zagreb Stock Exchange

LatAm

South America's top ten:

1. Gilson Finkelsztain, CEO, B3
2. Cicero Augusto Vieira Neto, COO, B3
3. Aime Ruiz Sacristan, Chairman, BMV
4. Jose Oriol Bosch Par, CEO, BMV
5. Leonardo P. Gomes Pereira, Chairman, Comissao de Valores Mobiliarios, IOSCO Board
6. Jaime González Aguadé, President, Comisión Nacional Bancaria y de Valores, Mexico, IOSCO Board
7. Andres Ponte, Chairman, ROFEX
8. Lilian Del Carmen Rocca Carbajal, Chairman, Superintendencia del Mercado de Valores, IOSCO Board
9. Diego Fernandez, CEO, ROFEX
10. Bruce Butterill, Executive Director, ACSDA

Africa

A fascinating aside about the African members, three of the top four this year are women while the richest man in the continent is tenth in terms of continental exchange influence:

1. Nicky Newton-King, CEO, JSE
2. Oscar N. Onyema, CEO, Nigerian Stock Exchange, President ASEA
3. Eleni Gabre-Madhin, CEO, Eleni
4. Nonkululeko Nyembezi-Heita, Chairman, Johannesburg Stock Exchange
5. Akinwumi Adesina, President, African Development Bank
6. Geoffrey Odundo, CEO, Nairobi Securities Exchange
7. Sunil Benimadhu, CEO, The Stock Exchange of Mauritius
8. Zeona Jacobs, Director Marketing & Corporate Affairs, JSE
9. Edoh Kossi Amenounve, CEO, Bourse Regionale des Valeures Mobilieres
10. Aliko Dangote, President, Nigerian SE

Australasia

Australia & New Zealand has a top ten as follows:

1. Greg Medcraft, Chairman, ASIC, IOSCO Member of the Board
2. Rick Holliday-Smith, Chairman, ASX
3. Peter Hiom, Deputy CEO, ASX
4. Dominic Stevens, CEO, ASX
5. Michael Aitken, CEO & Chief Scientist, Capital Markets CRC
6. Peter Jessup, EVP, NASDAQ
7. David Morgan, Chairman, CHi-X Australia
8. Mike Aikins, CTO, Chi-X Australia
9. James Miller, Chairman, NZX
10. Ben Bucknell, CEO, OnMarketBookBuilds

Journalists

The following deserve the plaudits as they are the 'newshounds' managing the exceptional when it comes to delivering parish stories, sometimes in very specialist areas within the market structure itself:

1. Huw Jones, Journalist, Reuters
2. Philip Stafford, Editor FT Trading Room, FT
3. Mobis Phillipose, Journalist, Livemint
4. Will Mitting, Publisher, FOW
5. Enoch Yiu, Journalist, SCMP
6. Matt Levine, Columnist, Bloomberg View
7. Max Bowie, Editor, Inside Data Management
8. Jeff Kutler, Editor, GARP & II Columnist
9. Dan Barnes, Editor, The Desk
10. Michael Lewis – the echoes of "Flash Boys" still reverberate...

Eminences Grises

Eminence grise: "a person who exercises power or influence in a certain sphere without holding an official position."

This list is not for those with C-suite titles at major firms. Rather it comprises people who may often not have the limelight – indeed many actively shun it! – but who can really make a difference. Thus they have influence:

1 Martin Watkins EY EMEIA Lead for Exchanges and FMIs

2 Ulf Axman Head of Sales Cinnober

3 Brian Healy Irish Stock Exchange Director of Traded Markets, Development, Operations

4 Nick Collier Global Head of Government Relations Thomson Reuters

5 Laurence Walton Director of Exchange Regulation & Compliance ICE Futures Europe

6 Hannes Takacs Senior Manager Local Currency and Capital Markets Development EBRD

7 Guy Simpkin Head of Business Development BATS Europe

8 Dr Miroslav Budimir SVP Eurex

9 Paul Bowes Director Benchmarks Thomson Reuters

10 Antonella Amadei Head of Global Development Market Infrastructures LSEG

11 David Grayson Co Founder & CEO Auerbach Grayson & Company

12 Jurg Spillmann Member of the Board Eurex

13 Phil Bruce Member of the Board ICE Futures Europe

14 Richard Seaman Chairman Xactium

15 David Feltes Market Infrastructure Consultant KPMG

16 Tom Krantz Senior Advisor Capital Markets Thomas Murray

17 Jorge Alegria Financial Market Advisory Consultant

18 Peter Cox Bourse Consult

19 Jake Pugh Independent

20 Henri Bergstrom Advisor for Business Development Abu Dhabi Securities Exchange

21 Mary Ann Callahan Paxos Market Infrastructure Advisor

22 Ian Dudden Global Content Director Agriculture S&P Global Platts

23 Jonathan Seymour Market Structure Bloomberg

24 Ann Berg Independent Commodities Expert

25 David White Riskapital Advisors CEO

Acronyms

360T	360T Trading Networks
A2X	A South African exchange aiming to compete with incumbent JSE
ABX	Allocated Bullion Exchange
ACSDA	Americas' Central Securities Depositories Association
ADGM	Abu Dhabi Global Market
ADX	Abu Dhabi Securities Exchange
AEMO	Australian Energy Market Operator
AeRO	The SME platform for the Bucharest SE (BvB)
AESO	Alberta Electric System Operator – Canada
AFE	Arab Federation of Exchanges
AFEX	Associated Foreign Exchange
AFM	The Association of Futures Markets – an emerging derivatives markets organisation
AFM	The Netherlands Authority for the Financial Markets, Netherlands, The
AFME	Association for Financial Markets in Europe
AFX	American Financial Exchange
AGROBOLSA	Honduras Commodities and Services Exchange
AHCX	AHL Commodities Exchange Ltd.
AIFX	Astana International Financial Exchange
AIX	Alternative Investment Board
ALTX Africa Group	ALTX Standing for "Alternative Exchange"
AMF	Autorité des Marchés Financiers
APCS	Austrian Power Clearing and Settlement
APX	Asia Pacific Exchange
APX-ENDEX	Dutch Power Exchange now owned by ICE
ASE	Amman Stock Exchange
ASIC	Australian Securities and Investments Commission
ASIFMA	Asia Securities Industry & Financial Markets Association
ASX	Australian Securities Exchange
ASX Group	Australian Securities Exchange
ATHEX	Athens Exchange Group (Hellenic Exchanges)

ATS	Alternative Trading System – now more termed MTF
ATS Brazil	Americas Trading System Brasil
B3	BM&F BOVESPA & CETIP merged to become Brasil Bolsa Balcao
BADEX	Bond and Derivatives Exchange
BaFin	Bundesanstalt für Finanzdienstleistungsaufsicht
BAISA	National Commodities Exchange, Panama
BATS	BATS stands for "Better Alternative Trading System"
BBA	British Bankers Association
BBVB	Baku Interbank Currency Exchange
BCBA	Buenos Aires SE
BCCE	Buon Ma Thuot Coffee & Commodity Exchange
BCE	Budapest Commodity Exchange
BCLP	La Plata Stock Exchange
BCSE	Belarusian Currency and Stock Exchange
BDEX	Big Data Exchange
BEX	Bond Electronic Exchange
BGC	Bernard Gerald Cantor
BIDS Trading	Originally stood for Block Interest Discovery Service
BIS	Bank for International Settlements
BIST	Borsa Istanbul
BISX	Bahamas International Securities Exchange
BIVA	BIVA is in the throes of creating a new Mexican stock exchange
BJCE	Bangladesh Jute and Commodity Exchange Ltd
Bloomberg ALLQ	Bloomberg All Quotes
BM&F BOVESPA	Now B3 the old name for the main Brazilian exchange
BME	Bolsas Mercados Españoles
BMFMS	Romania's Sibiu Monetary Financial and Commodities Exchange, later SIBEX
BMV	The Mexican Stock Exchange
BNY Mellon	Bank of New York Mellon
BOAG Borsen	The Hanover and Hamburg exchanges merged to become BOAG.
BODIVA	Angolan Debt and Securities Exchange

BOX	Boston Options Exchange
BRIX	Brazilian Intercontinental Exchange
BRM	Romanian Commodities Exchange
BRVM	Bourse Regionale des Valeures Mobilieres
BSCE	Belarussian Currency and Stock Exchange
BSE	Bombay Stock Exchange
BSE	Budapest Stock Exchange
BSE	Baku Stock Exchange
BSE	Bombay Stock Exchange
BSP Regional Energy Exchange	Serbian and Slovenian Power market
BSSE (in Slovak: BCPB)	The Bratislava Stock Exchange
BTA	Brian Taylor Associates
Buba	Bundesbank
BUCE	Belarusian Universal Commodity Exchange
BvB	Bucharest Stock Exchange
BVC	The Colombia Stock Exchange
BVL	Lima Stock Exchange in Spanish (also LMA)
BVM	Montevideo Stock Exchange
BVM	BVM – Bolsa de Valores de Moçambique
BVMAC	Bourse des Valeurs Mobilières de l'Afrique Centrale
BVMT	Bourse de Tunis
BVPASA	Asuncion Stock Exchange (Paraguay) (Bolsa de Valores y Productos de Asunción)
BX	Berne Exchange
CAISO	Power Market in California, USA
CAMMESA	Argentine Power Market
CASE	Central Asian Stock Exchange (Tajikistan)
Cavex	Wine Exchange based in the UK
CBEX	China Beijing Equity Exchange
CBMX	China Beijing International Mining Exchange
CBOE	Chicago Board Options Exchange

CBOT	Chicago Board of Trade
CCEE	Camara de Comercializacao de Energia Eletrica – Brazil
CCP	Central CounterParty Clearing House
CDBL	Central Depository Bangladesh Limited
CDS	Credit Default Swaps
CDSL	Central Depository Services Limited
CEESEG	CEE Stock Exchange Group
CEGH	Central Europe Gas Hub
CEINEX	China Europe International Exchange
CENACE	Centro do Control de Energia – Mexico
CEPS	Centre for European Policy Studies
CESC	China Exchange Services Company (Sino-HK jv on index creation etc)
CETIP	CETIP was the bond clearing and settlement house in Brazil, now part of B3
CFFEX	China Financial Futures Exchange
CFTC	Commodity Futures Trading Commission
CHEX	Cannabis Hemp Exchange
CISE	Renambed CISX (Channel Islands) then CISE now TISE
CISI	Chartered Institute for Securities & Investments (UK)
CISX	Channel Islands SE now TISE
CLO	Chief Legal Officer
CLOB	Central Limit Order Book
CLS	Continuous Linked Settlement – a core mechanism for settling forex transactions
CLTX	Cleartrade Exchange
CMA	Capital Market Authority
CMCRC	Capital Markets Cooperative Research Centre
CME	Chicago Mercantile Exchange
CME TR	CME Trade Repository
CMU	EU Capital Markets Union
CNMV	Comisión Nacional del Mercado de Valores
COLLEX	The Collateral Exchange
COMDAQ	COMDAQ Metals

COMDAQ	Can also refer to a vendor of exchange software
COMESA	Common Market for Eastern and Southern Africa
COMEX	Commodity Exchange (both collective term & refers to NYMEX subsidiary acquired by CME)
CONSOB	Commissione Nazionale per le Società e la Borsa, Italy
CRME	Commodity and Raw Materials Exchange
CROPEX	Croatian Power Exchange
CSD	Central Securities Depositary
CSD Iran	Central Securities Depository of Iran
CSD Macedonia	Central Securities Depository Macedonia
CSD Morocco	Maroclear the CSD for Morocco
CSE	Chittagong Stock Exchange
CSE	Colombo Stock Exchange
CSE	Cyprus Stock Exchange
CSE	Canadian Securities Exchange (ex Canadian National Stock Exchange – CNSX)
CSE	Calcutta Stock Exchange
CSRC	China Securities Regulatory Commission
CSX	Cambodia Securities Exchange
CSX	Cayman Islands SE
CSX	Cambodia Securities Exchange
CTX	Carbon Trade Exchange
CU Lending Exchange	The Credit Union Lending Exchange
CVM	Comissão de Valores Mobiliários, Brazil
DAH	Digital Asset Holdings
DB1	Deutsche Börse
DBS Bank	The Development Bank of Singapore
DCE	Dalian Commodity Exchange
DCV	Chilean CSD
DelphX	Credit Market / Bond Platform
DFM	Dubai Financial Market
DG Comp EU	EU Directorate General of Competition

DGCX	Dubai Gold and Commodities Exchange
DIFC	Dubai International Financial Centre
DJIA	Dow Jones Industrial Averages
DLA	DLA Piper law firm
DME	Dubai Mercantile Exchange
DMM	Designated Market Maker
DODAQ	A still born diamond exchange
DPM	Designated Primary Market Maker
DRW	Trading company founded by Don R Wilson
DSX	Douala Stock Exchange
DTCC	Depository Trust & Clearing Corporation
DV Advisors	Derivatives Vision Advisors
DW SEF LLC	A Tradeweb SEF with an anonymous CLOB
EACH	European Association of CCPs
EACH CCP	– same as above, also EACHCCP.eu
EBRD	European Bank for Reconstruction and Development
EBS	Electronic Broking Services now part of NEX
EC / EU	European Commission / European Union
ECB	European Central Bank
ECCAS	Economic Community of Central African States
ECN	Electronic Communications Network – forerunner to ATS and MTF
ECSE	Eastern Caribbean Securities Exchange
ECX	Ethiopia Commodity Exchange
EEX	The European Energy Exchange (owned by DB1)
EFSA	Egyptian Financial Supervisory Authority, Egypt
EGM	Enterprise Growth Market
EGX	Egyptian Stock Exchange
Egycomex	Egyptian Commodities Exchange
EIB	European Investment Bank
EMEA	Europe Middle East & Africa
EMEX	Energy Market Exchange, based in Houston Texas

EPEX	European Power Exchange
EPIAS	Energy Exchange Istanbul
EPIAS	Turkish Power Exchange
ESCO	Electricity System Commercial Operator
ESMA	European Securities and Markets Authority
ETS	Eurasian Trade System Commodity Exchange JSC
Euro TLX	Italian based bond MTF
EuroCCP	European Multilateral Clearing Facility
EuroTLX	An Italian retail / odd lot bond platform, part of LSE Group under Borsa Italiana
EWSM	The European Wholesale Securities Market
EXAA	Energy Exchange Austria
EXAA AG	the Austrian Energy Exchange
EY	Ernst & Young
FCA	Financial Conduct Authority
FEAS	Federation of European and Asian Stock Exchanges
FESE	Federation of European Securities Exchanges
FEX	Financial & Energy Exchange
FI	Financial Institutions
FIA	Futures Industry Association
FIAB	Federación Iberoamericana de Bolsas
FICC	Fixed Income Commodities & Currencies
FINMA	Swiss Financial Market Supervisory Authority
FINRA	Financial Industry Regulatory Authority
FITS	Fixed Income Trading System – bond market subsidisary of Indonesia SX
FMA	Financial Market Advisory
FMA	Finanzmarktaufsicht – Austrian regulator
FMDQ	FMDQ OTC Securities Exchange
FMI	Financial Market Infrastructure
FORTS Russia	The RTS Futures & Options Exchange
FOW	Futures & Options World now Global Investor Group
FSB	Financial Stability Board

FSC Korea	Financial Services Commission/Financial Supervisory Service
FSE	Fukuoka Stock Exchange
FSMA	Financial Services and Markets Authority, Belgium
FT	Financial Times
FTIL	Financial Technologies (India) Limited
FTSE	Financial Times Stock Exchange Indices
FTSE Group	LSE Index arm merged with Frank Russell Indices
GainTX SEF	A forex based SEF
GARP	Global Association of Risk Professionals
GreTai	Division of Taipei Exchange
GCSA	GCSA is a specialized underwriter and program sponsor of collateral, liquidity, and risk-transfer products for financial institutions and Financial Market Infrastructure
GCX	Ghana Commodity Exchange
GFI	IDB Group founded 1987 by Michael "Mickey" Gooch now owned by BGC
GFI	Global Financial Institutions
GFIM	Ghana Fixed Income Market, a division of the Ghana SE
GFMA	Global Financial Markets Association
GICEx	Georgia International Commodity Exchange
GLX	Global Listing Exchange
GME	Gestore dei Mercati Energetici
GME	Italian Energy Exchange
GMEX	Global Markets Exchange Group
GPW	Warsaw Stock Exchange
Greece HDAT	Regulated market for Greek government securities
GS	Goldman Sachs
GSX	Gibraltar Stock Exchange
GTX SEF LLC	Gain SEF
GXG Markets	Defunct Scandinarian SME exchange
Hi-MTF	Retail oriented Italian bond MTF
HKEX	Hong Kong Exchanges & Clearing
HKMEX	Hong Kong Mercantile Exchange (defunct)

HNX	Hanoi Stock Exchange
HOSE	Hochiminh Stock Exchange
HROTE	Croatian Energy Market Operator
HUPX	Hungarian Power Exchange
IBEX	Spanish Stock Exchange Index
IBEX	Independent Bulgarian Energy Exchange
ICAP	IDB now split between NEX and TP ICAP
ICDA	International Commodities Derivatives Association (formerly SFOA)
ICDX	Indonesia Commodity and Derivatives Exchange
ICE	Intercontinental Exchange
ICEX	Indian Commodity Exchange
ICGN	International Corporate Governance Network
ICMA	International Capital Market Association
IDB	InterDealer Broker
IDEM	Italian Derivatives Market
IDX	Indonesia Stock Exchange
IEX	The Investors Exchange
IEX	Indian Energy Exchange
IFB	Iran Fara Bourse
IGEX	Indo Global Exchanges
IHS Markit	Originally stood for Information Handling Services
II	Institutional Investor
IIA	Index Industry Association
IMAREX	International Maritime Exchange
IME	Iran Mercantile Exchange
IMF	International Monetary Fund
INE	Shanghai International Energy Exchange
INX	India International Exchange
ION	– actually NOT an acronym, just a three letter word
IOSCO	International Organization of Securities Commissions
IPSX	International Property Securities Exchange

ISDA	International Swaps and Derivatives Association
ISDX	ICAP Securities & Derivatives Exchange – now NEXexchange
ISE	Irish Stock Exchange
ISLA	International Securities Lending Association
ISX	Iraq Stock Exchange
ITG	Investment Technology Group Inc.
JADE	Joint Asian Derivatives Exchange
Jasdaq	Japanese name with a hat tip to NASDAQ, aimed at SME shares
JCCH	Japan Commodity Clearing House
JFX	Jakarta Futures Exchange
JOE	Japan OTC Exchange
JPX	Japan Exchange Group
JSE	Jamaica Stock Exchange
JSE	Johannesburg Stock Exchange
KACE	Kenya Agricultural Commodity Exchange
KASE	Kazakhstan Stock Exchange
KB Tech	Specialist UK vendor for exchanges and markets
KBB	Bratislava Commodity Exchange
KCE	Konya Commodity Exchange
KCG	Knight Capital Group
KDD	Slovenian CSD
KDPW	Central Securities Depository of Poland
KELER	Hungarian CCP & CSD
KICE	Kazakh International Commodity Exchange
Konex	Korea New Exchange
KOSDAQ	Korean SME Exchange part of KRX aimed at tech / SME stocks
KPMG	Klynveld Peat Marwick Goerdeler
KRX	Korea Exchange
KSE	Khartoum Stock Exchange
KSE	Kuwait Stock Exchange
KSE	Kyrgyz Stock Exchange

LAGIE	Hellenic Electricity Market Operator
LBMA	The London Bullion Market Association
LCH	London Clearing House
LFB	LIBOR Financed Bond – the first swap future (launched by LIFFE 1990's)
LIBA	London Investment Bankers Association – now AFME
LIFFE	London International Financial Futures Exchange
Liv-ex	UK based wine exchange
LJSE	Ljubljana Stock Exchange
LMA	Lima Stock Exchange
LMAX Exchange	London FX exchange
LME	London Metal Exchange
London DX	London Derivatives Exchange
London Merc	London Mercantile Exchange
LSE	London Stock Exchange
LSEG	London Stock Exchange Group
LSX	Lao Securities Exchange
LuSE	Lusaka Stock Exchange
LuxSE	Luxembourg Stock Exchange
MAE	Mercado Abierto Electrònico leading Argentine electronic securities & forex market
MAS	Monetary Authority of Singapore
MATba	Mercado a Término de Buenos Aires
MATCH	TriAct Canada Marketplace
MAX Exchange	A US residential mortgage trading platform
MBO	Management Buyout
MCDR	MISR for Clearing Depositary & Registry
MCE	Moscow Commodity Exchange
MCX India	Multi Commodity Exchange of India
MCX-SE	now MSEI
MCX-SX	now MSEI
MERVAL	Mercado de Valores de Buenos Aires
MEX Nepal	Mercantile Exchange Nepal Limited

MexDer	Mexican Derivatives Exchange
MEXM	Mercantile Exchange of Madagascar
MFSA	Malta Financial Services Authority
MGEX	Minneapolis Grain Exchange
MIAX Options	Miami International Securities Exchange, LLC
MICEx	Multi Commodity Exchange
MICEX	Moscow Interbank Currency Exchange (now part of MOEX)
MINDEX	Gold Exchange initiative (Mauritius)
Misr	Egyptian CSD
MKK	Merkezi Kayıt Kurulusu (Turkish CSD)
MNFME	Moscow Non-Ferrous Metals Exchange
MM	Market Maker
MMI	Modern Markets Initiative
MNSE	Montenegro Stock Exchange
MOED	Merger of Equal Desperation – epithet applied by Patrick L Young to the unsuccessful attempt of DB1 to acquire LSEG in 2106-2017.
MOEX	Moscow Exchange
MOU	Master of the Universe
MOU	Memorandum of Understanding
MSCI	An Index company where MSCI stands for "Morgan Stanley Capital International" which also owns Barra Indexes
MSE	Macedonian Stock Exchange
MSE	Maldives Stock Exchange Company
MSE	Malta Stock Exchange
MSE	Moldovan Stock Exchange
MSE	Mongolian Stock Exchange
MSE	Mozambique Stock Exchange
MSE	Maseru Securities Exchange
MSE	Malawi Stock Exchange
MSEI	Metropolitan Stock Exchange of India (formerly MSXI originally MCX-SE or MCX-SX)
MSXI	now MSEI

MTF	Multilateral Trading Facility – looks like an exchange, smells like an exchange but is not quite an exchange...
MTS	Bond trading platform begun in Italy, owned by Borsa Italiana (LSEG)
MX	Montreal Exchange now part of TMX
N2EX	NordPool day ahead electricity marketplace
NADEX	Northern American Derivatives Exchange
NAMEX	National Mercantile Exchange
NAMFIN-X	Namibia Financial Exchange
NASDANQ	A play on NASDAQ for an exchange trading in internet memes!
NASDAQ	National Association of Securities Dealers Automated Quotations
NASDAQ OMX	former name of NASDAQ after acquiring OMX
NBOT	National Board of Trade
NCDEX	National Commodity and Derivatives Exchange of India
NCSEX	Nizhny Novgorod Currency and Stock Exchange
NCX	Nigeria Commodity Exchange
NDC	Azeri CSD
NDX	Nordic Derivatives Exchange
NEEQ	Chinese National Equities Exchange and Quotations
NEPSE	Nepal Stock Exchange
NEX Group	The Michael Spencer electronic-centric IDB spun out of ICAP.
NFEX Markets	a new planned metal derivatives exchange planned by former LME CEO Martin Abbott
NFX	Nasdaq Futures Exchange
NGCP	National Grid Corporation of the Phillipines
Nilex	Nile Stock Exchange
NLX	NASDAQ London Exchange – a copycat futures exchange which failed
NMCE	National Multi Commodity Exchange of India
NOREXECO	Norwegian paper and pulp exchange
NSD (Russia)	National Settlement Depository (Russia)
NSE	National Stock Exchange of India (sometimes NSE India)
NSE	National Stock Exchange (USA)
NSE	Nairobi Stock Exchange

NSE	Nigerian Stock Exchange
NSE	Nagoya Stock Exchange
NSE Kenya	Nairobi Securities Exchange
NSX	Namibian Stock Exchange
NSX Australia	National Stock Exchange of Australia
NXCHANGE	Amsterdam based startup / SME exchange
NYIAX	New York Interactive Advertising Exchange
NYMEX	New York Mercantile Exchange
NYSD	Blockchain fintech company looking at exchanges and clearing
NYSE	New York Stock Exchange
NZX	New Zealand Exchange
OCC	The Options Clearing Corporation
OCX	OneChicago
OKTE	Short-term electricity Market Operator (Slovakia)
OME	Osaka Mercantile Exchange
OMIE	Operador do Mercado Ibérico de Energia
OMIE & OMIP	The Iberian Energy Derivatives Exchange
OMIP	Portuguese Energy Exchange
OMT	Outright Monetary Transations (by a central bank – AKA QE)
OMX	Scandinavian exchange group acquired by NASDAQ to form NASDAQ OMX
OPCOM	Romanian Gas and Electricity Market Operator
OpenBondX	A Bond platform based in the USA
OSC	Ontario Securities Commission, Ontario
OTASS	BIST Debt market
OTC Markets Group	Platform for OTC stock trading
OTC	Over The Counter – as in bilateral derivatives and / or non-public stocks which are traded.
OTE	Czech electricity and gas market operator
OTF	Organised Trading Facility, EU sibling of MTF
PACDEX	Pan-African Commodities & Derivatives Exchange
PanXchange	Pan Africa Exchange

ParFX	Par Foreign Exchange – a Tradition platform
PDE	Panama Diamond Exchange
PDEx	Philippine Dealing and Exchange
PDQ	PDQ runs Coda block trading facility for US equities
PDS	Philippine Dealing System Holdings Corp PDEx holding co.
PEGAS	EEX natural gas platform
PEMC	Philippine Electricity Market Corporation
PEX	Palestine Exchange
PFTS Stock Exchange	Ukrainian Stock Exchange
PMEX	Pakistan Mercantile Exchange
PoC	Proof of Concept
PolPX	Polish Power Exchange
POSIT	ITG block trading platform
Prop-X	Global Property Trading Exchange
PSE	Philippine Stock Exchange
PSX	Pakistan Stock Exchange Limited
PXE	Power Exchange Central Europe
QCA	Quoted Companies Alliance
QE	Quantitiative Easing
QSE	Qatar Stock Exchange
QSE	Quito Stock Exchange
R3	A Blockchain cooperative of banks and others
RASDAQ	Defunct (essentially replaced by AeRO) Romanian SME market
RBA	Reserve Bank of Australia
RBI	Reserve Bank of India
RBC Capital Markets	Royal Bank of Canada Capital Markets
RBOT	Rosario Board of Trade
RCE/BRM	Romanian Commodities Exchange
RCG	Rosenthal Collins Group
RCX	Rajkot Commodity Exchange

Regis-TR S.A.	Spanish Trade Repository
RGM	Quantitative trading firm
RMX	Risk Management Exchange, Hannover
ROFEX	Rosario Futures Exchange
RSEB	Royal Securities Exchange of Bhutan
RTS	Russian Trading System
SAOC	Muscat Clearing & Depository
S&P Dow Jones Indices	Standard & Poors Dow Jones Indexes
S&P Platts	Commodity arm of S&P
SAFE Asia	South Asian Federation of Exchanges
SAFEX	South African Futures Exchange now part of JSE
SASE	Sarajevo Stock Exchange
SEBON	Securities Board of Nepal
SCE	Sofia Commodity Exchange
SCH	Shanghai Clearing House
SCIEX	Samara Currency Interbank Exchange
SCMP	South China Morning Post
Scotex	Scottish Stock Exchange (proposed)
SDC Jordan	Securities Depository Center
SDiX	Singapore Diamond Exchange
SEBA	Securities and Exchange Brokers Association of Iran
SEBI	Securities and Exchange Board of India
SEBON	Securities Board of Nepal
SEC	U.S. Securities and Exchange Commission
SEC Malaysia	Securities Commission, Malaysia
SEC Nigeria	Securities and Exchange Commission, Nigeria
SECP	Securities and Exchange Commission, Pakistan
Seed CX	Seed Commodities Exchange
Seedrs	Seedrs – a leading UK crowdfunding platform
SEELink	A linkage of exchanges in the SEE funded by EBRD

SEF	Swap Exchange Facility
SEEPEX	South East European Power Exchange
SEM	The Stock Exchange of Mauritius
SEMO	Single Electricity Market Operator
SEN	Columbia Electronic Trading System
SEND	Corporate debt market of BME
SET	The Stock Exchange of Thailand
SETL	Pronounced Settle – Blockchain CSD vendor
SFC	Securities and Futures Commission, Hong Kong
SFOA	Swiss Futures & Options Association (now ICDA)
SGE	Shanghai Gold Exchange
SGPMX	Singapore Precious Metals Exchange
SGX	Singapore Exchange
SGX AsiaClear	Singapore Exchange OTC Clearing
SHFE	Shanghai Futures Exchange
SI	Systematic Internaliser (ie an MTF platform where banks cross their order flow)
SIBEX	Sibiu Stock Exchange
SICEX	Siberian Interbank Currency Exchange
SIFMA	Securities Industry and Financial Markets Association
SIFMU	Systemically Important Financial Market Utility
SIX	The Swiss Exchange Group and information vendor
SKOFX	South Korea Options and Futures Exchange
SME	Small and Medium Sized Enterprises
SMV	Superintendencia del Mercado de Valores, Peru
SENAF	BME platform for Spanish government debt
SPBFE	St. Petersburg Futures Exchange
SPCEX	St. Petersburg Currency Exchange
SPE	Slovenia Power Exchange
SPIMEX	St. Petersburg International Mercantile Exchange
SPSE	South Pacific Stock Exchange
SSE	Sapporo Stock Exchange

SSE	Shanghai Stock Exchange
SSEFC	Shanghai Shipping Freight Exchange
SSEV	Santiago Stock Exchange Venture Market
SSX	Sydney Stock Exchange now APX
SSX	Swaziland Stock Exchange
STOXX	DB1 Index company
STT	Securities & Trading Technology
SZSE	Shenzhen Stock Exchange
Tadawul	Saudi Stock Exchange
TAIFEX	Taiwan Futures Exchange
TASE	Tel Aviv Stock Exchange
Tashkent RSE	Tashkent Republican Stock Exchange
TCC	The Clearing Corporation – formerly BOTCC & allied to CBOT now ICE & CDS-centric
TCX	Tanzania Mercantile Exchange sometimes also TMX
TFEX	Thailand Futures Exchange
TFX	Tokyo Financial Exchange
TGE	Polish power exchange, also PolPX
TGE	Tokyo Grain Exchange – now closed
TIFFEX	Tokyo International Financial Futures Exchange – TFX pre-2007
TISE	The International Stock Exchange – title once used briefly by LSE
TISE	The International Stock Exchange – rebranded Channel Islands Stock Exchange
TME	Tehran Metal Exchange
TMR	Thomson Reuters
TMX	Toronto Montreal Exchange
TNB	TNB Transmission Sdn Bhd Malaysia
TOCOM	Tokyo Commodity Exchange
TOM MTF	The Order Machine
TP ICAP	Tullett Prebon ICAP
TPEX also GreTai	Taipei Exchange (GreTai Securities Market)
tpSEF Inc	Tullett Prebon SEF
TR	Trade Repositary

TRFIT	Thomson Reuters Fixed Income Trading
Trop-X	Seychelles Stock Exchange
TSE	Tehran Stock Exchange
TSX	Toronto Stock Exchange now part of MX
TTSE	Trinidad and Tobago Stock Exchange
TUGE	Tajik Universal Goods and Commodity Exchange
TurkDex	Turkish Derivatives Exchange
TW SEF LLC	The Tradeweb fully disclosed SEF (as opposed to DW SEF)
TWSE	Taiwan Stock Exchange
UBS	Union Bank of Switzerland, created from the merger of UBS and Swiss Bank Corporation
UBS MTF	Stock MTF of UBS
UCE	Ugandan Commodities Exchange
UCEM	Universal Commodity Exchange of Moldova
UCX	Universal Commodity Exchange
UEMOA	L'Union Economique et Monétaire Ouest-Africaine
UICE	Ukrainian Interbank Currency Exchange
USE	Uganda Securities Exchange
USEX	Ural Regional Currency Exchange
UWIN Corp	Unleashing the Wealth of Nations – fintech company with attitude...
UX	Ukrainian Stock Exchange
UZEX	Uzbek Commodity Exchange
VOB	BIST derivatives market
VolX	The Volatility Exchange
WACMIC	West African Capital Markets Integration Council
WCE	Winnipeg Commodity Exchange
WFE	World Federation of Exchanges
WGC	World Gold Council
WGT	Warsaw Commodity Exchange
WMBA	Wholesale Markets Brokers Association
WSE	Warsaw Stock Exchange (also GPW)
XM	Colombian power market, a subsidiary of Colombian state transmission company ISA

Y-COM	Yokohama Commodity Exchange
Yercomex	Yerevan Commodity and Raw Material Exchange
YSE	Yangon Stock Exchange
YSX	Yangon SE – Myanmar (Burma)
Zamace	Zambia Agricultural Commodities Exchange
ZAR X	ZA stands for South Africa, R for Rand. ZAR X is a new South African Stock Exchange licensed in 2017
ZCE	Zhengzhou Commodity Exchange
ZIMACE	Zimbabwe Agricultural Commodity Exchange
ZSE	Zagreb Stock Exchange
ZSE	Zimbabwe Stock Exchange

Exchange Invest FAQs

FAQs

Q What Is Exchange Invest?

A Exchange Invest is the unique daily newsletter devoted to the world of exchanges and market structure. Originally devised as a means to help investors better understand what was happening in market structure, the online email delivered newsletter has rapidly become the benchmark daily read throughout the world of market structure.

Q Who Created Exchange Invest?

A Exchange Invest was the brainchild of Patrick L. Young, a former exchange CEO and advisor to investors in market structure. When investors were complaining that there was no single source they could read to stay abreast of exchange news and analysis, Patrick was inspired to create the daily Exchange Invest newsletter.

The core faculties of the newsletter are the pith and insights overlaid upon daily headlines which are themselves gleaned by a rather complex technological process which broadly blows the minds of those who are privy to the details, so we keep that proprietary data private. Suffice to say it started simply enough and has become a myriad of complex IT approaches ever since, thanks to various wondrous geeks who themselves have written code for leading marketplaces across the world.

What differentiates EI in its approach from conventional media is:

1. Practitioner led content, driven by the founder's 30 years' experience in markets;
2. A willingness to deliver praise where it is merited and in many ways, perhaps more significantly:
3. A firm belief that criticism must be applied where something is not sound, sensible or up to scratch.

NB The third point is taken very seriously, very seriously indeed. To that end, it has been a fascinating journey, particularly the bits where Exchange Invest called out some errant incumbents and had to listen to what amounted to feedback which was little more than ludicrous tantrums. Even from the other side of major oceans, toys exited prams with such a terminal velocity that it was difficult to know whether to laugh or cry at the sheer inability of seasoned executives to realise they had not only been called out but that Exchange Invest was not about to change its tune whether it involved threats, cajoling or, well, whatever. At this point, like all exhausted babies, said parties have (mostly) stopped bleating. Exchange Invest loves nothing more than a dose of repentance and a new direction. Some have maintained their stubborn paths while others have come to realise Exchange Invest is an "honest broker." EI praises the good in any situation, even in those instances where there may be issues about the person(s) behind it. Some parishioners have come full circle and to go back to the original point, Exchange Invest would much, much rather praise than criticize.

Q Er, "parishioners?"

A Correct! The world of exchanges and market structure is insufficiently valuable in pure money terms to justify being a "sector" per se (like automobile manufacturing or pharmaceuticals) and moreover, while global, it is sufficiently small that you tend to see a lot of the same faces across the globe at industry gatherings. Therefore Patrick describes the market infrastructure industry as a parish as it feels like a relatively close knit and modestly sized community... Market structure is a parish and clearly therefore, those within it are the parishioners.

NB This does not infer there is an ArchBishop / Cardinal or other diocesan leaders above the parish per se, although some may clearly have their own views/delusions on the matter...

Q Has Exchange Invest Delivered A Sound Track Record of Prediction of Industry Trends?

A The track record of Exchange Invest has been pretty staggeringly accurate (better than its founder ever expected!) at foreseeing the outcome of industry events. For instance, Exchange Invest noted the industry would see a deregulatory wave coming up four years before President Trump's election began the new deregulatory cycle while, with low latency prescience, it was noted that the latest (please, God, make it the last!) Deutsche Boerse attempt to buy the London Stock Exchange – the 'Merger of Equal Desperation' as Patrick termed it – would fail. Exchange Invest was vastly ahead of the Brexit curve and much more. Equally, as regards matter which Exchange Invest got wrong, the news was almost always favourable. The redemption of Euronext after ICE left it to its own devices was as unexpected as it was joyful to the parish. To see that such a dysfunctional cluster of politicking exchanges could turn into a dynamic business in a new independent guise was a lovely thing to get wrong.

Exchange Invest continues to deploy the same analytical toolkit to look forward to industry developments.

Q How Much Does Exchange Invest Cost?

A Exchange Invest remains at its core a free newsletter and if you're not reading it, you should not be surprised if you aren't in the 1000 most influential figures in the parish!

Q How Does Exchange Invest Make Money?

A Exchange Invest is free to read but supported by some key industry sponsors (to whom many thanks!). It also has a Premium Subscription service which costs 300 US dollar per annum while there is additionally the Exchange Invest 1000 which, as you likely know if you have read this far...is also sold separately.

Moreover if you are not reading the Exchange Invest Premium Content you most probably struggle to be ahead of the influence curve...

Q What is biggest concern facing the exchange industry?

A Exchange Invest is optimistic. Worryingly many exchange executives appear perma-pessimistic at dealing with the opportunity around them which they struggle to cope with.

About The Author

Patrick L Young is the Author of "Capital Market Revolution!' and several other books. A specialist in derivatives since early in his career, Patrick has subsequently expanded across multiple other business/ financial subject areas. He has written extensively on the future of finance at the intersection of digital technology for at least a decade. That is a decade, if not two, before the phrase "fintech" was even coined.

A former exchange CEO and director of various entities, Patrick is an experienced entrepreneur and a leading advisor to investors in the world's financial markets structure.

Young is the Founder and Publisher of Exchange Invest, the Daily newsletter of the global 'parish' of market structure.

You can find out more about Patrick L Young at PatrickLYoung.net

About the Publisher

DV Books is publishing this tome under its Exchange Invest Imprint

DV Publishing is a specialist publisher of financial books
while Exchange Invest is best known for publishing the daily newsletter of market structure world wide.

DVBooks.com

ExchangeInvest.com

Afterword

So the world's bars may have gone broadly smoke free but at least now you have an answer to that age old question of just who are the most influential people in the exchange and market structure parish.

I have no illusions that this list will have pleased all of the people all of the time but it was a first attempt intended not to please anybody but rather to calculate a general pecking order of importance according to influence.

The next Index has already begun being compiled. The second annual volume will appear in mid 2018 and various improvements in the Index and this book are already being planned.

All feedback good or bad will be most welcome. If I may however request a little structure to the remarks that would be appreciated – justifications and explanations will always be welcomed. Moreover, there is absolutely NO doubt that some very deserving parish souls have been omitted. You are welcome to champion their good names whether they are you or merely you friends / colleagues /relatives or merely vague associates.

Please direct any correspondence to myself Patrick L Young via Patrick@DerivativesVision.com

Thank you for reading and I wish you a wonderful year. If we don't meet face to face, let's at least try to catch up via the Exchange Invest daily newsletter of market structure (free subscription via ExchangeInvest.com) and of course in the second volume of this index of influencers which is now open for 2018 entries ...not to mention advance orders and advertising / sponsorship opportunities.

PLY

Index of Names

Index of Names